D1105223

X Laurence L. Whitenack

A TRAIL IS NEVER COLD

THE LIFE AND TIMES OF SHERIFF
JESS SWEETEN
by Lawrence Melton Jr.

Published by

Ballycastle Publishing Company
2120 Ballycastle Street
Dallas, Texas 75228

Copyright © 1995 Lawrence L. Melton Jr.
ISBN 0-96648819-0-X
All Rights Reserved
MANUFACTURED IN THE UNITED STATES OF AMERICA

Table of Contents

Dedicated to my Father
Lawrence L. Melton Sr.
and the Memory of my Mother
Mary June

Introduction

Sheriff Jess Sweeten arrived in Henderson County, Texas at a time of blood and dying. It was the thirties: a decade of unparalleled lawlessness in the history of our nation. He was a young man, barely twenty-four, but he brought special equipment for the job: two hundred pounds of rock-hard muscle, a dedicated spirit, iron fists and a pair of Colts .45 automatic pistols.

During Sweeten's first term in office the McGehee family of four were reported missing from George Patton's fifty-four acre farm—roughly eight miles north of Athens, Texas.

The farmer told Sweeten that two men, supposedly friends of the McGehee family, drove out to his place late one night around midnight and honked the horn. He said, J. W. McGehee ran outside and talked with the two men. According to Patton, they talked for about five minutes, then J. W. ran back into the house very excited and said to his wife, "Honey, get up and get your duds on, we're headed to the oil-fields."

That was Thanksgiving Day, 1932.

In those days a lawman relied solely on his common sense and dedication. Jess was dedicated. He traveled the back roads day and night, searching for leads and scraps of information that often led nowhere. The state had no crime lab. Criminologists were unheard of in those days, and he had one outside deputy to cover the largest county in east Texas, with a population of thirty-five thousand. But in a period of slightly more than three years, this "Boy Sheriff" had solved eight perfect crime murders.

In his amazing twenty years as sheriff of Henderson County, Texas, Jess had solved a total of eighteen murder cases. He solved all the cases involving hijacking by firearms and eighty-five percent of all burglaries. When he retired in 1954, there were no unsolved murder cases; no unsolved stick-up or hijacking cases. Not a single rape case went unsolved while he was sheriff of Henderson County.

Jess Sweeten's record stands as one of the finest records of achievement in the history of law enforcement.

When a crime was committed in Henderson County, Jess took it personally. And when Mrs. Florence Everett pleaded with the young Sheriff to find her missing family, Sweeten was true to his word. It took nearly four years of hyper kinetic determination, but Jess Sweeten got his man.—

Mention his name to the old-timers of Henderson County and you'll hear stories that, at first, will sound as though they're pulling your leg. They say he could track a minnow through a swamp on a moonless night in a drizzling rain. Others will tell of the time he placed an ad in the Police Gazette inviting Machine Gun Kelley, Bonnie and Clyde, Pretty Boy Floyd, John Dillinger, and host of others to meet him in Henderson County for a final shoot out.

Raymond Hamilton (a member of the Barrow gang) confessed to a Dallas newspaper that Clyde and Bonnie always avoided Henderson County because of Sweeten's reputation. He said they drove through there only once. It was the closest they ever came to being captured.

They'll say he could lick five times his weight in wild-cats, and swallow the meanest outlaw—whole raw or cooked.

"He had four sets of jaw teeth!" said an old-timer at the auction barn. "And with holes punched for more!" said another.

Pat O'Brian, the movie actor, summed him up this way: "I had always wanted to meet him. I was looking for this rough and tough Texas sheriff that I had been reading about—then, in walks this well dressed gentleman with a voice that could put a baby to sleep. But I knew his quiet manner only masked the caged dynamite that could be unleashed at a moment's notice."

Once an outlaw had a rifle aimed squarely at Sweeten's head, and before the man could squeeze the trigger, Jess had pulled his pistol and fired three slugs in the man's chest. The outlaw died instantly.

Jess was half Irish and Cherokee. He stood six foot four and a half inches tall —seven foot even if you count the boots and hat. He had a total of eleven gun battles. but only three of those eleven had to be killed. "It was kill or be killed," he said.

Introduction

Henderson County Courthouse

FOREWORD

by *Myrtle Sweeten Rolfness -age 95*

My brother, Jess Sweeten was named after my great grandfather, Jessie James Sweeten, who owned a cotton plantation near Holly Springs, Mississippi. It was a very large operation and took thirty-two slaves to operate.

His son Marion; that was our grandfather, left the plantation and moved to the "Nations" sometime around 1860. Then, in 1866, the union regulators red flagged the Sweeten plantation for paying taxes to the wrong government. I'm not rightly sure about the date, but it was shortly after the civil war.

Grandfather Marion and his wife, Harriet, homesteaded 160 acres of land between the Cherokee Nation, with it's capitol to the northwest at Tahlequah, and the Chocktaw Nation with it's capitol to the southeast at Tuskahoma.

Several years later, Judge, Issac Parker persuaded Marion to become a Deputy U.S. Marshall. He rode circuit on a "tumbleweed wagon" which consisted of a driver, a cook and two out-riders. It was a rolling jail and had large four-inch rims on heavy oak wheels.

One time, Marion and several other Deputies took Belle Starr to Ft. Smith in the wagon after she had been identified as the leader of a band of horse thieves. Belle was unaccustomed to being treated disrespectful; so when an officer turned his head, she threw all the food and cooking utensils out the back door—one item at a time. This caused the deputies to back-track for miles.

After that incident, Marion and the other deputies chained Belle to the floor of the rolling jail and bounced her around for fifty miles. When they brought her before Judge Parker, the judge ordered her to take a seat. She refused. "Your honor, my butt is so sore I couldn't sit on a feather pillow. I'll just stand if that's alright with you!"

She remained standing throughout the trial.

After serving time in a federal prison up in Ohio, Belle offered two-hundred dollars to a Chocktaw named, Willard Walking Sky, to kill deputy Marion Sweeten. Marion took a .38-40 slug to his chest and died while crawling toward my grandmother, Harriet who had been ambushed by Jack Spaniard near the road.

When my father, John Alexander, who was only sixteen at the time, learned that Jack and Willard were responsible, he swore to kill them. And that included Belle Starr.

After the funeral, which was attended by many of the townsfolk, my father sold the farm for the price of a good horse, a shotgun, a brace of colt's pistols and a .30-30 rifle, then rode east in a pouring rainstorm.

He found, Willard Walking Sky three days later in a cabin near Winding stair mountain. He called him out and fired two slugs in Willard's chest before he could clear leather. Jack Spaniard was found in the small town of Tuskahoma, and when the smoke cleared, Jack's carcass lay face down in a wagon rut.

The last on John Sweeten's list was Belle Starr. He never admitted to killing Belle, but he told us how she died. He described in detail the clothes she was wearing at the time. "She was killed the same way mother was killed," he said. "By ambush." One blast from a shotgun to the back which knocked her from the horse, then a single shot from a .45 to the back of her head." The event occurred three miles north of her small cabin at Younger's Bend. "She was on her way home riding side-saddle and never knew what hit her." Then he smiled and said, "They thought Edward did it."

Edward was Belle Starr's son.

Grandmother and grandfather are buried in Wapanucka, Oklahoma. My father John Alexander became a Federal Marshall a few years later, and my brother, Jess followed in their footsteps. Jess was the youngest, most famous sheriff that Texas ever had. This is his story.

A TRAIL IS NEVER COLD

The Life And Times Of Sheriff Jess Sweeten
1932-1954

O dimming trails of other days,
Your lure, your glamour, and your ways
Will last while those who knew you live.
And fading to the past will give,
To guard and to forever hold,
A wealth of stories never told.

for:

Hazel, Jessie Nell, and Peggy Ann Sweeten

Henderson County Jail January 1949

THE BATTLE OF TRINIDAD

Trinidad, Texas -1929

Trinidad is located halfway between the Trinity River and Cedar Creek near the far western edge of Henderson County. In 1929 it boasted a population slightly above two hundred and fifty people. It was a farming community with two major crops—corn and cotton. It had two cotton gins, two churches, a school and a new $7,000,000.00 power plant under construction near the river. A row of businesses paralleled the Cotton Belt railroad tracks to the north: Messrs. Daniel & company, T.J. Trotman and Son, T. M. Johnson, Pulley Drug, Mellar Motors, Bradley's garage, and the R. D. King restaurant.

Most of the roads in this area of East Texas were made of dirt and gravel. They were impassable during the rainy season, so the state went on a huge road building campaign.

New bridges were being built over Cedar Creek, and a large concrete bridge had almost spanned the Trinity River to the northwest. Overnight this sleepy little community had fifteen hundred construction workers storming into town looking for a good time.

Heat lightning flashed in the darkness as Jess sat quietly under the shadow of the depot. He was an iron-worker for the Otis Elevator Company, and for the past few months had helped install the elevator at the new power plant. His next job was a high-rise in Kansas City, and he was supposed to be there no later than the following Monday. The trip would take about two days so he had plenty of time if he left that Friday night.

He continuously checked the clock in the drugstore while rolling cigarettes from a cloth sack of Golden Grain Tobacco. A flat-bed truck lumbered into town from the north; squatting low to the mud-covered street under the weight of no less than twenty construction workers. The driver carefully aimed the truck up the street until several workmen pounded their fists on top of the cab near the pool hall.

A few drenched workers entered the smoke filled parlor but most ran toward the blinking lights of a bootlegger's Model-T Ford.

Suddenly, more trucks entered from the south and Trinidad came alive. Static-filled music of the Carter family could be heard from a distant radio, and a red lantern was placed in the window of Aunt Lillie's whorehouse.

The sad music was interrupted by sounds of laughter followed by a couple of howling dogs and a few braying mules from the nearby stable.

The bootlegger peddled sour-mash whiskey for three dollars a quart, and Aunt Lillie auctioned the girls anywhere from two to three dollars—depending on their conformation. A good fleshy lap-sitter would bring five, but after sinning with a hundred men a week they were scarce as hens teeth.

Unlike Corsicana, Trinidad was a boom-town without a drop of oil. Its luck came in the form of new highway construction; but like any prosperous town, it always attracted men of unsavory character.

Scrap-Iron Johnson was such a character. Within a space of ten minutes, he had downed a pint of whiskey, then walked to the middle of the street and began urinating in a mud puddle, intentionally exposing himself to a woman who quickly turned her head then ran inside the cafe.

Johnson bellowed at the top of his voice. "I'm rough and I'm tough and I'm hard to bluff. I rode in here on a cyclone whipping it with a rattle snake! I wuz raised in the backwoods and suckled by a poley bear! I got a double coat of hair, steel ribs and a barbed wire tail; and I don't give a damn where I drag it! Do any of you ladies want to love me?"

Foghorn Clancy, the new deputy constable, vowed to clean up the rats nest, so he and a good number of the local businessmen were discussing ideas at a big round table in the cafe. But when the woman ran inside complaining about the sex fiend in the middle of the street, Foghorn figured a good pistol-whipping would be a proper dose of medicine.

Johnson was the slip operator on the new highway between Corsicana and Athens. At night he was an undefeated prize-fighter. Without a doubt, Johnson was the toughest of the lot. He could work two Clydesdale horses half to death by day, then whip as many as ten men at night, and all for five bucks a throw.

Foghorn informed the town elders that he had a lot of experience dealing with blow-hards like Johnson. And to demonstrate that fact, he quickly walked up behind the big wind-bag and lowered the boom, hitting Scrap Iron as hard as his fifty-nine year old arm could swing his pistol.

But Johnson didn't go down.

The blow had no effect on the big road worker. Johnson turned facing the surprised constable with a wolfish grin then pointed to his chin and said, "Now hit me right here."

Foghorn quickly obliged, knocking Johnson backward. Again Johnson wouldn't go down. He quickly stepped up to the constable pointing toward his forehead.

"Now, hit me right up here."

Foghorn's face had turned the color of cotton as he slammed the barrel of the pistol across Johnson's forehead.

Again Johnson smiled.

"Now hit me over here!" he said, pointing to a spot above his left ear.

Suddenly, and without words, Foghorn holstered his pistol then turned on his heel and walked slowly toward his car, tossing the badge on the porch of the cafe before driving away.

Bob King, the owner of the cafe, nodded as though he understood. He retrieved the badge, then silently walked back into the cafe.

Suddenly, Johnson was joined by two flunkies, Bluford Fletcher and Lowell Morehouse, who began chunkin' rocks at the newly retired constable who by this time, had turned north past the cotton gin. Johnson rewarded the flunkies with a long thirsty drink of whiskey then began to bellow loudly:

"I got a tombstone heart and a graveyard mind! I'm a mean ol' boy and I don't mind dyin'! I drink Coke, smoke rope, shoot the bull with the old folk! But I don't play! I tore up a radio because it did play! I live on tough street! The farther you go, the tougher it gets. And I live in a dugout at the end of it!"

Jess noticed several more businessmen storm the cafe aiming insults in the direction of Bob King, the man who had hired the coward in the first place. Jess could not hear what was said but, from the red faces and bulging neck veins, he could tell they had a real problem on their hands. And he knew something else, nothing had changed. It was just a typical Friday night in Hell's Junk Yard.

The last gun in Trinidad was hidden in ol' Joe Dyer's fancy railroad jacket. He was the night watchman for the railroad and his duty was toting the mail pouch from the post office to the depot. It was a simple job, but lately the stress of the job had given the old man stomach ulcers. And a strange rash had worked its way from his belly button to his backbone.

He hid in the shadow of a parked automobile until Johnson's back was turned before making his run toward the depot. But unknown to the old watchman, Johnson had spotted Joe long before his meeting with Constable Foghorn. In fact, Joe was the fellow that Johnson had been waiting on in the first place. Constable Foghorn was just an added bonus.

Johnson had intentionally positioned himself near the mud hole, knowing that sooner or later, Joe Dyer would make his run toward the depot.

Johnson's two flunkies, Bluford and Lowell moved directly behind the night watchman as he quick-stepped across the street. Johnson quickly stopped the old man directly in front of the large puddle. Bluford and Lowell blocked any hope of retreat.

Joe's attempt at masking the fear of Johnson was betrayed by a quivering upper lip that stuck to his front tooth. "I don't want no trouble." Joe pleaded in a high-pitched squeaky voice, "I've got to get this mail sack to the depot over there!...it's agin' the law for you to stop the mail! This here's guvmint' property!"

"Ye hear that?" Johnson snarled as he eased closer to the old man. "He don't want no trouble!" Johnson placed a hard calloused hand on Joe's shoulder then spun him around to face Lowell. "Ye' see ol' Lowell there? He don't want no trouble either!...and Bluford! Hell, he's just a little ole pussy cat when it comes to trouble. But me!" He grabbed hold of Joe's chin with his left hand and squeezed his lips grotesquely. "Now I want me some trouble."

Suddenly, and without thinking of the consequences, Joe went for his .38 pistol. Johnson quickly released his grip then slammed a right cross to Joe's chin which sent the old man to the ground. Lowell kicked the gun from his hand.

"Souie!" yelled Ace as Lowell tossed the pistol to Johnson. He grabbed the old man by both legs dragging him back and forth through the mud puddle.

"Wake up, you bunch of crow bait!" Johnson yelled, "We're gonna kick in yer winders and cave in yer doors! And treat them young ladies like a bunch of dammed whores!"

Joe staggered to his feet but lost his balance and fell forward. "Let him up," Johnson hollered, "and I'll show you how to hit a railroad bull!"

Bluford positioned the helpless old man directly in front of Johnson who hit him with a hard right which sent ol' Joe Dyer splashing mud.

Jess Sweeten had seen enough. He tucked his suitcase under the wooden bench then stepped from the shadow of the depot. He walked directly toward the three thugs then stopped roughly an arm's length and slightly to the right of Scrap Iron Johnson. Then with a voice calm as a dry river bed, he said, "Now help him to his feet and give him his gun."

Johnson turned to face the strange sound coming from somewhere above his head and noticed a six foot four and a half inch man-mountain, with arms the size of tree trunks.

Bluford found himself following Lowell's shadow which was inching its way toward the crowd near the pool hall. The calm tone in Sweeten's voice was giving him goose bumps big as nickels. It was a smooth voice. The kind that didn't have fear mixed in with the words.

Johnson noticed a good sized crowd of construction workers assembling across the street and somehow he had to save face. He bravely spat on the ground beside Jess's boot: "And if I don't?" he growled.

The conversation dried up. Jess Sweeten hit Scrap Iron with a hard right cross that sent him sliding a full three feet past ol' Joe Dyer. And it was the last thing Johnson would remember until he regained consciousness a few days later. Johnson's lower jaw had been fractured with a single rock-hard punch, and six of the man's teeth had been knocked out.

Jess pried the pistol from Johnson's hand while Lowell and Bluford quickly began wiping mud from Joe Dyer's jacket. "We wuz' just having a little fun that's all," Lowell said sheepishly.

"Well, the fun's all over. Pick up your friend and get him to a damn doctor."

Bob King had been watching the action through the window of the cafe and giving his fellow businessmen a blow-by-blow description of the fight. When Johnson fell, Bob King yelled so loud that several patrons thought it was a robbery.

"He's down!" Bob hollered. "The bastard's out colder'n a banker's heart."

Tom Trotman scampered to the window and cupped both hands against the glass for a better look. "Is he dead?"

Bob was jumping with excitement. "It's close enough for me! Let's get a shovel and bury the som-bitch."

Mr. Pulley ran to the door adjusting his thick glasses high on his nose. "Who's the fellow that hit him?"

Bob's legs were twitching with excitement. "I don't know. I never seen him before, but he's a businessman. Yes-sir, one hell of a businessman."

According to Reverend Hopkins, who was peeking through the screen door, it was all the Lord's doing. And the splinters in his knees proved that he had done his part. He had prayed many times for the Lord to save Johnson's soul, but it hadn't worked. His last prayer however, was for the Lord to take Johnson way off some where out of town and just knock him in the head.

The reverend warned his flock every Sunday about the fish-mouthed politicians who drove all the way from the state capitol to brag about the construction. "Prosperity," said the politician, "is good for business. Why, the new buildings will go up so fast the shadders can't keep up!"

Reverend Hopkins took pride in the fact that he had been right all along. According to him, the bootlegging and gambling business was doing very well. The snake-oil salesman stood on the corner and made a fortune selling cocaine laced cure-alls in funny-shaped little green bottles. Irish vacuum cleaner salesmen stormed in from Dallas telling women that company scientists learned that dust-mites had caused more deaths than the black plague—and it was their duty to inform them that a vacuum cleaner was the only way to get rid of the varmints.

Boarding house rent doubled overnight. And now, thanks to the politician, the ugliest lap-sitter in Trinidad made more money than the new doctor. And the doctor wasn't needed until one of Lillie's girls spread some strange dose of sickness faster than the snake oil could cure it.

The town hero was leaving on the night train and the local businessmen began to worry as to how they were going to pin a badge on that scrapper; and they had less than ten minutes to map a plan. Bob King worked good under pressure so he was volunteered to go over to the depot and stall the fellow.

The train had already pulled into the depot and time was short, so they pushed Bob out the door and watched him long-stride to the depot before the train screeched to a stop.

He had roughly eight minutes left to make a pitch without seeming to beg so he paused briefly to study the train schedule, not wanting to appear too foreword in his approach. Besides, it would give him a second or two to catch his breath.

"Where you headed?" Bob asked.

Jess turned around to make sure Bob was not talking to someone else before he answered. "Kansas City."

Bob eased inched a little closer and nodded as though Kansas City was a pretty good place to go. "Got a job up there I suppose?"

"Yes, sir."

This iron worker not only was a big man; he was a right friendly critter. And polite. Which was good because Trinidad, Texas was badly in need of friendly critters.

Sweeten's gaze remained focused on the conductor, and was ready to hop aboard as soon as the man gave the signal. Mr. Bob King talked a little faster as he worked his way between Jess and the doorway.

"We saw what you did to ol' Junk Iron over there."

"Well, he had it coming!"

Bob smiled nervously. "Boy, I agree with that. We all agree, and that's why I want to talk to you. Truth is, we need somebody to do a little more of that around here."

Jess lit a cigarette as he inched toward the door of the passenger car. "Well, I hope you find one."

Bob leaned against the door. "We'll pay you a hundred and forty dollars a month."

Jess gave the ticket to the conductor. "That's a lot of money."

"And you get free room and board on top of that."

"Yes, but I have good job."

"And you get four dollars for each arrest." Bob had the iron-worker's attention.

"Look," Bob said, "there's another train in the morning. Why don't you sleep on it? One night at least."

Jess noticed another fist-fight breaking out near the pool hall, and farther up the street near the filling station several men were shooting an illegal game of craps under the street light. He could see the bootlegger selling whiskey to men waiting in a long line. Suddenly, more trucks loaded with road workers entered town.

Aunt Lillie had a line stretching nearly halfway around her house. And with a little bit of finger counting, Jess estimated the lawbreakers numbered somewhere around twenty men. It didn't take an expert in arithmetic to figure his take would be somewhere in the vicinity of eighty bucks. That was a lot of money.

"Well, let me think about it."

Hoping he had been successful in the parley, Bob shook Jess' hand and introduced himself. He returned to the cafe and quietly waited with his friends until the train steamed its way out of town.

They waited until the last car cleared the depot before looking out the window. The room was silent except for the fervent prayers of Reverend Hopkins who sat with his open Bible at the corner table.

A full three minutes had passed. The depot was empty. Apparently, Jess Sweeten was on his way to Kansas City. Beads of sweat appeared on the brow of Reverend Hopkins as he prayed harder. Several more minutes passed, then suddenly the door opened.

The big iron-worker walked to the large round table where the businessmen sat silently drinking coffee. He spoke in the same quiet manner he'd used when approaching Scrap-Iron Johnson. "I'll be a little rough."

The smiles on the faces of Trinidad's elite was so wide that any one of them could have eat a banana sideways.

"Figured you might be," Bob said. "I'll take you over to Malakoff in the morning and let Constable Al Leopard swear you in."

Jess nodded politely then turned to walk away. John Trotman, the owner of the dry goods store, stood reverently with his hat in his hand and asked, "How old are you son?"

Jess stopped at the door then answered in the same polite manner. "Twenty two—."

PART TWO

Constable Albert Leopard was an eighty-year-old lawman who was born in 1849—roughly thirteen years after the battle of the Alamo, and when Bob King and Jess arrived at the lawman's home, he was sitting in his front porch rocker with a hot cup of coffee in one hand and a saucer in the other.

Albert poured a small amount of coffee in the saucer then blew it cool enough to drink. It was the proper way to drink coffee in those days. He sipped loudly from the saucer as Bob King led the young deputy constable up the path toward his front porch.

"Well, come on up and sit a spell," Albert shouted as he spat a long stream of chewing tobacco toward a chicken.

"Is this the fellow you said could break a trace-chain with his teeth?"

Bob King smiled, then introduced the two.

"Jess," Bob said proudly. "This is Constable Al Leopard. He's the fellow who collects the money around these parts. If you need advise he's the man you call. If he tells you he seen a chicken dipping Levi Garrett, look under its wing and you'll find the can."

The old constable was a walking history book on law enforcement. He had spent the better part of his eighty years on the back of a horse. And, as he said, "Using his back for a mattress and his belly for a blanket."

After drinking a pot of coffee, Al learned that Jess was Marion Sweeten's grandson. So, he told a story about the time he traveled the Nations with Marion Sweeten, Heck Thomas and Tyner Hughes. All of whom worked for Hanging Judge, Issac Parker, in Ft. Smith.

Albert was one of three deputies who had curry-combed the Nations looking for the killers of, Marion Sweeten and his wife. He began to laugh when he said that, Tyner Hughes was the only deputy marshall who had ever been invited to eat at Belle Starr's home.

After supper, Tyner Hughes told Belle that she had cooked the best meal he had eaten in over a month. It was so tasty in fact that he asked for the recipe. Belle let out a belly laugh and said, "Tyner, that was a damn five-foot rattle snake I killed three days ago. Now go puke the som-bitch up and get the hell off my property!"

Al Leopard said they had covered the whole part of eastern Oklahoma looking for Willard Walking Sky and Jack Spaniard but somebody killed them before they got there.

'But times are changing. These pulp peddlers are writing as though Belle Starr was some kind of hero, when in fact, she was a cold bloodied killer, a horse thief and whore to boot. In fact, one of her lovers impregnated Belle's daughter, Pearl while Belle was in Ft. Smith."

Jess was a good listener, and Al knew him to be made of pretty good stuff. Still the lad had some learning to do. He handed Jess an old .38 Smith and Wesson then ordered the young lawman to the back yard. He'd learn him how to shoot the old way, before some two-handed squatter got a hold of him.

"Eastern cops," he said, "is learned to grip the pistol with two hands and hunker down like a skeered rabbit—which is nearly foolish. My common sense tells me that them squatters couldn't scatter a pile of horse-shit with a two-dollar rake."

He walked over to the trash barrel in the back yard and began poking around for a number-303-size empty can. He dug around for a few seconds, then found what he figured was a good one. He walked to the shed and dragged a saw-horse to the edge of the barbed wire fence and positioned the can near the center.

"Son let's see if you can hit ol' Del right in the Monte. Give me three shots, and watch yer' toes."

Albert stepped off fifteen paces after pausing to work his snuff with a sweet-gum branch. He winked at Bob King and said, "Use one hand. And fire from the hip." He turned, facing Jess with a grin which was akin to a jackass eating thistles. "Just do the best you can, son."

To the old man's surprise, Jess stepped back another five paces and positioned his right leg slightly foreword to offset the recoil of the pistol. He drew and fired three rapid rounds which struck the can dead center in a slightly off triangle pattern—each hole no more than a quarter-inch apart.

Bob and Albert had heard only one sound, but they were surprised when they counted the hole. Albert didn't believe him. He asked Jess to eject the shells in his hand so he could count them. Sure enough, three spent casings dropped in his hand.

Jess gave them a shooting demonstration that many would later pay to see. He split playing cards at twenty paces, then knocked the spots off the five of clubs with the pistol held upside down. He held a snuff bottle in his out-stretched right hand, let it drop, then drew and fired with the same hand, shattering the thing before it hit the ground.

The only advice Albert would offer Bob King after the shooting exhibition was this: "Bob, when you get back to Trinidad, you find the meanest som-bitch in town and tell him that hell's come to breakfast."

The standard procedure for a deputy constable was to make an arrest then drive the prisoner to Athens where formal charges could be made. The prisoner would be fined or, if a felon, he'd be jailed by the county sheriff. If the crime was a misdemeanor the deputy constable could collect the fine himself then turn the proceeds over to Albert Leopard, less the four dollars commission.

A constable, traditionally, was an older man with years of experience. He was a fellow to report that ol' So and So, did Such and such. The constable would hear the complaint then call the sheriff and ask for a deputy to come over and get old So and So. The Sheriff, when time permitted, would send his next available deputy—depending on the seriousness of the crime.

Henderson was the largest county in East Texas, with a population of over thirty-five thousand. The sheriff had at most three outside deputies who were running the county's dirt roads day and night. Trinidad was the hottest spot in the county and when Sheriff Joel Baker heard about Jess Sweeten, it almost tickled him to death. For the first time in over a year he could stop worrying about Trinidad and concentrate on the four hundred plus whiskey stills that had sprung up all over the county.

What Jess needed most was a jail, but that was out of the question. All available space in town slept as many as eight sweaty road workers, and quite a few slept in automobiles or wagons. He needed a secure holding room. One that would house twenty or so. Something about the size of a boxcar.

A boxcar?

Why not? he thought, *They're at least thirty-five feet long, and eight feet wide.* If the Cotton-Belt rail company would rent him one, he could have them park it on the side rail near the loading dock.

After several phone calls, he contacted a salesman by the name of Nicholson. "Sir, do you rent boxcars by the day, or do you rent them by the mile?"

"Either way." said Mr. Nicholson. "And you're very fortunate to catch me at the right time. It just so happens that we have a forty-foot cattle car out there in the yard. It come in last night with a bunch of them little bitty mules. I'm told they're unloading them this afternoon though. If you'll do the cleaning; that would save us a little money. So, I could let it go for the price of a thirty-five—which is very reasonable."

It was reasonable.

The general store chipped in a few piss-pots, and a local farmer was more than happy to donate twenty bales of moldy, chigger infested hay for the bedding. A fellow who worked at Mellar Motors painted a little sign above the door of the boxcar that said, "Trinidad Jail."

Within hours the new jail had become about as handy as a pocket on a shirt. A Negro named Jimmy Lightfoot was cornered by three red-haired brothers after betting a weeks pay they could throw a seven two times in a row.

They knew Jimmy Lightfoot had seventeen dollars in his pocket because they saw him purchase a quart of whiskey with a twenty dollar bill. The oldest brother ordered Jimmy to fork it over. It was a business deal. They would wisely invest his money in the crap game, and pay him a little interest if they won a few throws. But if he refused the deal, they'd hit him so hard his toenails would come loose.

Jimmy refused by quoting words the good-book said about such doings. "Neither a borrower nor a lender be."

Jess was at the barber shop when Jimmy staggered through the door bleeding like a dehorned cow. He had to find Mr. Jess before both his eyes swelled total shut. "Mista' Jess!" he hollered.

"I'm Jess. What's your problem?"

Jimmy lumbered toward the barber chair trailing blood on the newly polished marble floor. The barber quickly grabbed the Negro by the arm and led him outside.

"Nigger, don't come in here! Ta' hell's a matter with you? You think you can just sashay in a white man's place of business dripping blood all over the damn floor!"

"Mista Jess," Jimmy pleaded from the doorway. "Can you make dem' red-head peckerwoods gimmie my money back?"

Noticing the Negro ease another foot inside the door, the barber began to hone his razor.

"Nigger, you come back in here and I'll cut you from wishbone to appetite!"

Jess gave the barber a stern look which caused the red-faced barber to back away. He quickly stepped outside to hear the Negro's story. Jimmy turned his one good eye toward the barber. His smile exposed a mouth full of bloody teeth.

"Can you point 'em out to me?" Jess asked nonchalantly.

"Yes, suh," Jimmy said, pointing up the street, "they's up there 'tween the pool hall and the fillin' station."

Jess walked to the end of the block and cornered the three brothers who were throwing dice with several other men. He stood silently watching for a moment as a crowd appeared seemingly from nowhere to cheer for the brothers. Under the canopy of the filling station another crowd had gathered, but they were there to see how the new constable would handle his job.

The townsfolk saw the crowd tighten around Jess and the Negro as the three culprits were pointed out.

"Dat's him," Jimmy pointed. "And dem two wuz in on it," he said, pointing toward the other two brothers.

Jess asked the oldest brother to return the money, then looked toward the crowd that begun to tighten around them.

Big Red snickered and said, "Fellow, you ain't had that gun but one day! That ain't long enough for you to be telling me what to do."

Red had the crowd firmly on his side as the circle grew smaller. Suddenly, Jess tossed his pistol to the Negro and spoke loud so all could hear, "Jim I want you to take aim. If anybody in that crowd takes a step toward us, you shoot him! You hear me?...You shoot to kill!"

Jim proudly pointed the pistol toward the crowd, and with a high pitched, overly excited voice yelled, "Yessuh! One step and this ol' dog's gonna bark six times!"

Jess eased within arm's length of Big Red as the Negro pointed the pistol toward the crowd. The distraction was just enough to get the first lick on the oldest brother. Big Red hit the dirt. He was flat on his back and out cold. A left hook to another brother sent him to the ground. A crowd from the whorehouse joined the circle, shouting for Big Red to get up. The rest began cheering for the brothers.

Big Red staggered to his feet but, a straight right to the nose sent him to the red dirt for the second time. Once more Big Red staggered to his feet, and once more he joined his shadow. Jess just tapped him with a left hook and this time Big Red stayed down.

Jim was almost dancing as he walked the circle of rough construction workers pointing the pistol at a man who dared to step foreword. He stepped close to the smallest brother and said, "Mr. Little

Red, it's yo' turn to bat!" He aimed the pistol toward the crowd and shouted, "Dis' ain't yo' damn dance! Now you back on off. Mr. Jess needs room to work!"

Little Red was less inclined to scrap with the big Constable, but to save face he waded in with both fists flying. Jess dodged a wild right cross and countered with a left hook which connected, and Little Red joined his two brothers.

Jim yelled proudly, "Mista' Jess, you hit that boy so hard, when he wakes up his eyes be lookin' out his ear holes!" Jess collected the missing seventeen dollars from the pocket of Big Red's overalls.

Before the night was over, Jess had fought twenty times and arrested over a hundred men. He lost three good shirts in the deal, but the battle for Trinidad was over. Few would challenge him to a fist-fight in the future. Now he could go about the business of cleaning up the town.

The fines collected on his first day had set an all-time record. And when Al Leopard counted the night's take, it came to fourteen hundred dollars and some few cents. He thought Jess had robbed a bank. Albert said he had never seen that much money in his life. Jess Sweeten had earned four hundred dollars in commissions on his first day in office. That was a hundred dollars more than the county sheriff made in a month, but nobody complained. He had earned every cent.

Aunt Lillie left town rather than live in a boxcar. She had earned enough money to buy a fancy home on Swiss Avenue up in Dallas. She was happy to leave. Jess ordered the pool room operator to remove all the slot machines. The man refused, saying that they were the property of Richard Sigler, one of Henderson County's top lawyers. Jess removed them himself.

The bootlegger was arrested and fined fourteen dollars for each jar of whiskey. He had twenty-four jars so the fine came to three hundred and thirty-six dollars.

"Fear and respect are first cousins," his father once said. "If a man has no respect for the law, then you make him fear it! and when he does, you've won half the battle. But if a lawman backs down one time, he's dead —in more ways than one.

"THE DIRTY DOZEN"

A farmer loaned Jess a cattle truck to haul a load of hard case prisoners to the Athens jail, and by the time they arrived all twelve of men had learned four things:

1. It's hard to stand in fresh cow manure with both hands cuffed.
2. You can smear it but you can't wipe it.
3. The smell would gag a maggot on a gut wagon.
4. Jess Sweeten seemed to enjoy the way they slid in it.

Jess parked in front of the Henderson County jail, then walked to the sheriff's office with a fist-full of paperwork. The twelve prisoners remained shackled to the side-boards attracting blow-flies the size of hummingbirds.

Jess introduced himself to the jailer and proudly boasted that he had a load of prisoners that were anxious to get free room and board in the jail house. They were real hard cases, and figured the Judge would throw the book at them.

He was not exactly sure how the process of judging criminals worked, but if the jailer would kindly take them off his hands, he'd go back to Trinidad and fetch another load.

"What are the charges?" the jailer asked.

"Well, the three in the front whipped an ol' boy and stole his money. The two on the left come at me with a jack handle and a pocket knife; they'll need to see a doctor. I caught the three on the left talking vulgar in front of a young girl. I've already beat the hell out of them, but the Judge might want to send them on down to prison. And I told the four sneak-thieves in the back to get out of town, but as you can see, they didn't go."

The jailer chuckled at Jess's ignorance of the terminology. "Son, what you have here is misdemeanors. That's a fine anywhere from five to fifteen dollars. I wish I could help you. Why don't you take them over to Malakoff. The Constable can take the money."

"He's not there today. What about a Justice of the Peace or somebody like that?"

"Gone to church. This is Sunday"

"What about the Sheriff?"

"He went fishing over in Hot Springs, Arkansas. Won't be back until Monday morning."

"Can you keep them here until he comes back?"

The jailer smiled, "No. You'll have to bring them back Monday."

The bells of the First Baptist Church began to chime the first call to sinners as Jess angrily cranked the truck, jerking the clutch which sent the dirty dozen sliding to the floorboards. He aimed the big Dodge Brothers truck toward the church house.

Soft piano music echoed through the nearly filled auditorium as he led the twelve foul-smelling handcuffed prisoners to the back row. The elderly couple politely scooted to the far end of the pew, allowing room for the smelly sinners to sit together. Jess removed his hat then quietly ordered that all twelve should take a seat and be quiet.

The elderly couple graciously offered the men the entire back row to themselves after getting a nose full of how they smelled and an eye full of how they were dressed. To the prisoners, it seemed a right neighborly thing for the old couple to do, since Jess had failed to make a formal reservation.

Seconds later, the two rows in front of the prisoners began to crowd foreword. Perhaps for a better view of the beautiful blond who entered the stage from behind a large blue curtain near a bunch of other folks who were dressed in long robes.

Archie Noble, still suffering a hang-over and a sore jaw, mentioned that this particular young lady could crumble crackers in his night spot anytime. The other eleven began kissing the air in her direction as though it were her face.

The beautiful lady gracefully thumbed through the pages of a frayed hymn book with a pleasant smile, and then, upon finding a good song, told the congregation to turn to page twenty two.

Archie whispered under his breath, "And if any of y'all ain't got that page, you can turn to page eleven, and sang' it twice."

Big Red burst out laughing at the joke, and that caused a small girl with glasses thick as a coke bottle to turn around. The little brat was crossing her eyes, sticking out her tongue and holding her nose all at the same time.

The beautiful singer sang "Amazing Grace" with such clarity and emotion that several prisoners got misty-eyed, and took to hunting for pigeon in the rafters, all in an effort to hide tears. It was apparent that none of these jailbirds had ever seen the inside of a church—although Archie did admit to painting one back in twenty-two.

When the singer finished up, she walked back to her seat and not a single one of those stuck-up, steeple-people applauded that fine tuned voice.

"That ain't fair," Archie thought to himself; so he stood up and commenced to whistle and applauded as loud as he could, hoping the congregation would see the error of their ways and join in. That didn't happen. Apparently, the blood in the veins of these Bible-thumpers was more-than-likely cold enough to freeze a cat.

When Jess ordered they should sit down and shut up, Archie said, "Hell fire! Jess. These sons-a-guns are shunning that poor girl, and I ain't gonna set here and put up with that crap! What they need is a good butt whipping if you asked me! She's more than likely, gonna' go home and cry her eyes out over what they done to her."

When old Deacon Powell's eyes rubbered toward the back row, it set up a head-turning party that went on throughout the whole service. Women took to fanning themselves faster and faster, until the smell of perfume got so thick they had to open a few windows. Suddenly, the preacher sprang from his chair near the choir and began to shout and holler at the whol' bunch. The man's face turned beet red as he searched scriptures right and left in a frantic search for words to use against all of them.

When he read a few that brought some "amen's" from the front row crowd, he knew he had found the place to read. He held the Bible high over his head then told everybody to read the same words. "Matthew fourteen, verse forty one," he hollered.

"The son of man shall send forth his angels, and they shall gather out of his kingdom all things that offend, and them which do iniquity; and shall cast them into a furnace of fire: there shall be wailing and gnashing of teeth."

Two frail looking fellers jumped from their seats and hollered, "Amen, brother!"

When them two fellers jumped up, the preacher started prancing all over the stage as if the Holy Ghost had him by the collar. He aimed his Bible toward those same two fellers and hollered, "Do I hear an amen?"

He heard a lot of amen's.

"Cast not your pearls to swine!" he shouted at the top of his voice.

Amos gave the other prisoners a puzzled look and said, "Who in the hell would throw a string of pearls in a hog pen anyway?"

Jess slapped Amos on top of the head and ordered him to keep his mouth shut.

Near the halfway point, the same young lady tried again. And the second song was nearly as sad as the first. She sung as though her little heart would bust wide open at any minute; it was a song about wanting folks to go to the promised land with her.

Archie Noble got all choked up about it. Tears were streaming down his cheeks as he politely stood up and said, "Darlin', you just hang on. When I get out of this mess, I'll go with you."

Jess suffered the embarrassment until old Deacon Powell began to pass around the offering plate. But when he stopped one row short of the back row, Jess grabbed him by the arm. Some said that it was the first time in the history of the First Baptist Church of Athens that anyone had ever spoken in the unknown tongue. The old Deacon turned his pleading face toward the preacher as though they were trying to abscond with the money.

Jess ordered each prisoner to place fifteen dollars in the offering plate then returned it to the Deacon and led the prisoners outside.

The choir began to sing, "Just as I Am," and while all the heads were bowed; the preacher hurriedly ran out the door to greet the young constable.

"Son," he said, "what you did in the House of the Lord was the most unusual thing I've ever witnessed in my life. I've never seen anything like that in all my twenty years of preaching the gospel. But I want you to know that Training Union starts tonight at seven-thirty.

"THE SHARECROPPER"

Cephus Ates was a sharecropper from Jefferson, Texas who, early one morning, rushed into the house and told his wife to pack heavy. A white dove had circled him twice in the cotton field. It made a loud cooing sound then flew off toward the west. It was a sign; because both his mules stopped dead in their tracks and refused to plow another inch.

His mules were a little long in the tooth for such a journey, but he figured they could pull the wagon at least twenty miles a day if they were grained well, and not pushed too hard.

The ground around Jefferson was too hard anyway. The plow wouldn't sink no further than half a foot in that hard earth, and as far as he was concerned, the weeds and sticker burrs could reclaim the whole county.

As a boy, he remembered the deep, sandy loam soil around Trinidad. It would grow anything from whippoorwill pea to chinquapin. In fact, that area of Henderson County was known to have over seventy-one different varieties of trees; and God only knew how many crops that soil could produce.

He overheard a white man say that Trinidad was building a new power plant to produce electricity. And every house in East Texas would have the stuff within a year. According to the white man, electricity was piped into the house through a bunch of wires. And it was a cheaper than coal oil. But, like anything new, electricity had its drawbacks. If you touch a wire, you'd be graveyard dead in less than a minute.

These new lamps were nearly as hot as a coal oil lamp but it didn't burn with fire. The whole house was supposed to light up pretty near good as daylight; and to light em' up, you just turned a little knob-- being real careful not to touch a wire. It was something worth looking into, but he seriously doubted if he'd ever find a use for it. 'Cides, when night falls, it's time to go to bed.

Word of mouth led him to Pete Duffield's four hundred acre farm near the river, but they had spent several hours asking directions before finding someone who actually knew way. The farm was about four miles south of town on a narrow dirt road.

Minutes later, Cephus turned the mules west toward a fresh white-washed house with a garden that ran from the road to a stand of large black walnut trees near the front yard. It was one of the finest homes that Cephus had ever laid his eyes on. The large two-story Victorian home rested on high brick piers enclosed with white lattice. The huge covered porch spanned the full length of the house at the front, then ran almost halfway down the right-hand side, then ended at the outer door to the master bedroom.

Several pecan trees shaded the yard between the house and barn, while carefully tended rose bushes graced the well-manicured front yard. A hive of honey-bees sat near a stand of wild persimmon trees at the end of the garden.

This place is beautiful, Cephus thought as he reigned the mules to a halt near the porch.

The farmer and his wife were having morning coffee at a small white ornamental-iron table on the porch. The farmer's wife greeted the strangers with a pleasant smile, so Cephus set the brake. He wrapped the reigns on the brake handle, then slowly walked toward the porch.

His first impression of the farmer's wife was that of a front-porch gospel singer. She had pleasant blue eyes and long hair which was rolled in a large bun on the back of her head.

Cephus removed his hat as he walked to the corner of the porch—being careful to lower his head in a respectful manner. "Good mornin' to you sir."

"I's looking for Mr. Pete Duffield's place. Sho' hoping this is it cuz' it sho' is a fine place. Yes, suh! A mighty fine place."

Pete scooted his rocker around to face the Sharecropper and said, "My name is Duffield. What can I do you for?"

Cephus held his hat close to his heart as he looked toward the garden—avoiding direct eye contact so the farmer wouldn't think he was uppity.

"Well, suh! I's down at the Trinity Gin Company this mornin', and they tells me you looking fer croppers."

Pete rocked a little faster.

"You know about cotton, do you?"

"Yes, suh. Fair to middlin'."

"You know about bumble bee cotton?"

Cephus laughed softly, "Sho' do!...but we ain't plantin' that kind of cotton. Not on this place. No, suh!"

"Why not?"

"Too short. A bumble bee don't even have to fly. He can just walk down the rows sucking pollen."

After an hour questioning the Negro's farming ability, a deal was struck. The cotton would be farmed on the halves. Cephus would plow plant and pick for half the profits.

Pete Duffield would provide all the family needs until the crop was sold, which was the custom. Things such as flour, sugar, coffee, seed for his garden, wood for the cook stove, mule grain, rent and medicine. All of which would be kept in the tally book, and ciphered at picking time.

Cephus fenced a small garden plot behind a two-room shack that stood near the end of the field. The soil had a fertile taste near the fence, and he figured it would grow about anything they fancied, provided he could out think the cut-worms and rabbits.

It was the way he remembered it. The soil was deep sandy loam with a good layer of topsoil. Mr. Duffield's barn contained a never ending supply of fertilizer which he'd mix with bowley hulls from the cotton gin. Unknown to white folks, bowley hulls added extra sweetness to watermelons and cantaloupes. White folks burned hulls out of ignorance.

Cephus' wife surveyed the shack and found it to be no better or worse than the last. At least it was better than camping under a tree. And with a little elbow-grease and lye soap, she could make it liveable even though it leaned slightly to one side, and there were many cracks in the thin walls and floor. The walls could be covered with po'folks wallpaper which was made from the pages of old newspapers dipped in a flour paste.

The four girls and two boys scouted the river beyond the back field and found a plentiful supply of mustang grapevines for swinging; several wild pear, persimmon and chinquipin trees. The field contained a fair supply of bull-nettle that produced clusters of sweet nut pods. It was a place for high-on-the-hog living.

That night Cephus tuned his guitar, then leaned his raw-hide chair against the wall of the front porch and sang the only song he knew:

"The longest train I ever saw,
Went down the Georgia line,
 The engine passed at six o'clock,
And the cab passed by at nine.
 In the pines, in the pines,
Where the sun never shines,
 And we shiver when the
Cold wind blows.
 I asked my captain
For the time of day,
 He said he throwed his watch away.
A long stub ram and a short cross till,
 I'm on my way back home.
In the pines, in the pines,
 Where the sun never shines,
And we shiver when the
 Cold wind blows.
Little girl, little girl,
 What have I done,
That makes me treat you so?
 You caused me to weep, you
Caused me to morn,
 You caused me to leave my home.
In the pines, in the pines,
 where the sun never shines,
And we shiver when the
 cold wind blows."

It was good to hear the whippoorwill, and he would savor the promise of good fortune by waking the rooster on the way to the field, then resting when the mules were too tired to pull. There was an art to mule-plowing, and he would teach his boys something the white folks had no patience for. "When a mule balks, fetch him a pail of water and cool him down. Let him rest a spell. A Mule ain't stubborn. He jist stop to cool down."

When picking time drew near, Mr. Duffield's kindly nature had changed. He accused the boys of stealing firewood off his back porch.

Cephus knew he had not raised a pair of thieves. "This farmer," he told his boys, "is no different than all the rest. He's looking for a reason to change the deal, but he ain't goin ter git one."

He told the boys to cut a big stack of wood for the farmer. "Put it on his porch. He'll have to stay up late at night thinking up stuff."

The boys did as instructed, but the farmer said they left the gate open when they brought the wood to the porch. He complained that several milk cows got into his horse grain and would more-than-likely bloat themselves to death.

Cephus wanted no trouble this close to picking time. He offered to pay for both cows if they went belly up. He'd pay for all the grain once the crop was sold. But each day the farmer had a new gripe. He found several clumps of weeds growing in the cotton field and figured that alone cause the loss of five hundred pounds of prime cotton. Cephus had a good idea whose half the five hundred pounds would be subtracted from too. He was familiar with this type of ciphering since he had been in the cotton business all his life.

Pete Duffield walked to the edge of the field and found a batch of evidence. Two clumps of bunch-grass. He held the grass high, yelling as though he was stung by a scorpion, "What in the hell is this?" he yelled.

Cephus answered in a flustered whisper. "It's grass, Mista' Duffield."

The farmer gathered more evidence on the next row, then threw the clump of grass toward Cephus, "I treat you Niggers right and look what I find! If I ain't fighting weevils and cut worms, it's grasshoppers and shuffle-butt, lazy ass Niggers!"

He was busy now, searching the whole field for fresh evidence, then grabbing a handful of grass burrs. "Got Tammitt!" he yelled, then held his palm outward to show a trickle of blood. "Look at that! I fed you. I took care of your family. I put a roof over your damn head,— and now I have to see a damn doctor before I get the lockjaw!"

Cephus carefully pulled the grass burrs from the farmer's hand and tried to apologize but greed was spreading faster than a sweet potato vine. When the last burr was removed from the farmer's hand, so was Cephus. He and his family were ordered off the property. He had until noon to pack plunder or he'd have the law do it for him. There would be no splitting of the crop because the farmer said he'd be forced to hire expensive day-pickers.

Tears blurred the image of his wife standing in the doorway of the shack. His daughters were busy hanging clothes on the fence, and the two boys were feeding Mr. Duffield's yearling near the barn. A thousand blackbirds had gathered in a large oak near the creek—a sure sign winter was just around the corner.

All was lost. Cephus's legs trembled under the weight of his body as he ambled toward the shack. His wife knew something dreadful had happened because she noticed he had stopped halfway to the house and leaned across a fence post. His head was down as if he was in deep thought, or perhaps crying. A long time passed, but suddenly, and with renewed energy, Cephus boldly hollered for everyone to load the wagon.

"You boys hitch the team," he said firmly. He was a man by God, and he had a right to make a living for his family same as anybody. Half his life had been wasted trying to satisfy some greedy white farmer; but this time was going to be different. We'll see what Mr. Jess has to say about it, Cephus thought to himself.

His wife and four daughters quickly went to work, they neither complained or asked why, but they sensed a change in papa, and it felt good.

Within two hours the wagon was loaded and aimed toward Trinidad. He found Jess at the cafe and patiently waited in the wagon until he had finished his meal. If this white man was as fair as folks said he was, he'd know soon; because the story about Jimmy Lightfoot had spread through the black community like a prairie fire.

When Jess walked out of the cafe, Cephus quickly told him how the sharecroppers were being treated in Henderson County. He told the young constable that they had worked from sun-up to sun-down all year, then get run off for being lazy.

Jess had been listening intently, showing no outward sympathy with the sharecropper's plight until Cephus said the white man's reason had been that they were lazy.

A hard worker will have calloused hands, Jess thought to himself; so he walked over to the wagon and shook hands with each boy, purposely feeling their hands. *Each had hands rough as tree bark.*

"Turn the wagon around," Jess said bluntly, "and meet me at the farm."

Jess figured that he'd get there about fifteen minutes ahead of the sharecropper, which would be ample time to hear Mr. Duffield's side of the story. He turned down the narrow path that led to the house, and the farmer greeted him near the porch with a large smile and a tall glass of ice tea.

"Heard you lost your Niggers." Jess said nonchalantly.

"Yeah, I did. Got to find me some day pickers. Don't suppose you'd know where I could round up a few?"

Jess drank the ice tea rather quickly then tossed the ice toward the rose bushes, "What caused you to run them off?" Jess asked, as he walked toward the field.

"Jess, you know how a Nigger operates. You treat 'em good and they get lazy on you. Day's coming when you can't get a Nigger to work a'tall. I told them to chop the damn grass and weeds out of there a hunnert times. The damn weeds are taking my whole crop."

Jess walked along the edge of the field peering down each row. The field was white as snow—a bumper crop. And it was clean as a whistle. Mr. farmer was lying through his teeth.

"Y'all were sharecropping?"

"Yeah, and I'll never make that mistake again. You got to feed the 'em, buy their damn clothes, grain the damn livestock, stove 'em up all damn winter, and hope to hell you break even. Course you never do, but you keep on trying."

Jess nodded, then walked over to the shack. The farmer followed close behind the big Constable, stopping every so often to take a sip of tea. Jess stepped into the shack after testing the rotten floor boards by shifting his weight to each leg. The boards had buckled from a sagging foundation.

"Is this where they lived?"

The farmer threw the last of his tea out the window and said, "Yeah, and look at that...they broke all the winders out."

Jess noticed large cracks in the walls and ceiling.

"How do they keep warm in here?"

The farmer slapped his leg, then laughed loudly, "Son, a Nigger's hide is as thick as an alligator. Cold don't have no affect on a Nigger!"

Jess nodded as though he had learned something new, then walked outside after noticing the wagon turning up the road.

"Look at that! They're like bunch of damn homing pigeons! Jess, when they get up here, I want you to arrest the whole bunch for trespassing."

Jess opened the gate and started toward the wagon. "I told them to come back Mr. Duffield."

A worried look suddenly appeared on the farmer's face when he noticed Jess help Cephus' wife from the wagon. He did not see the constable wink at the children.

Jess suddenly turned, then looked sternly at the farmer and said, "Cephus, are you going to file charges against Mr. Duffield?"

"What are you talking about?" the farmer hollered.

"For theft, Mr. Duffield! If Mr. Ates files the charges, I'm taking you to jail. You admitted that you and Mr. Ates were sharecropping. In my book, sharecropping means that half this crop of cotton belongs to him. That's what we do to thieves Mr. Duffield. We put them in jail."

Jess again winked at the children as he waited for the red-faced farmer to figure a way out of the mess he had created for himself. The old man walked toward the fence, kicked a bottle at a chicken, then for a long time pondered his predicament while leaning on the gate post. Suddenly he walked back to the big constable and said, "Alright! he can stay for a little while—until I sell the crop, then I want all these damn Niggers out of here."

Jess leaned against the wagon and shook his head." You're not going to sell the crop, Mr. Duffield. When it's ready, you call me. We'll all go to the gin together. I'll split the money."

The farmer's wife had been listening from the porch. She walked into the house after hearing the outcome. Moments later, she surprised everyone by bringing a large silver tray out to the fuming crowd. It contained a large blue ceramic pitcher of iced tea and eleven glasses. She placed the tray on the tail-gate of the wagon as her husband glared defiantly toward her. She carefully filled each glass to the brim and began to pass them around.

"What in the hell are you doing woman?" Pete asked angrily.

"Shut your mouth, Pete!" she shot back, then continued serving. "Please forgive my husband," she said to Mrs. Ates. "You're welcome to stay here as long as you like...the old fool is wrong and he knows it. Besides I've enjoyed having you all out here. So, if you're willing to overlook the ignorance. Just put your stuff back in the house.

"TRAPPING THIEVES"

Articles in several newspapers began to appear about the young deputy constable after it was learned that he cleaned up Trinidad with his bare knuckles. Sheriff Joel Baker was so impressed with Sweeten that he made him a deputy sheriff.

When a problem arose in any town in Henderson County, Jess Sweeten was sent to put an end to it.

A grocer in Brownsboro continuously lost merchandise through a huge crack in the outer wall of his grocery store. The thief would widen the hole somewhat, then reach in and grab whatever was on the shelf. The grocer had repaired the hole many times but the thief used a crowbar to pry off each repair. Next morning, he learned the thief had made off with ten cans of expensive peaches.

The hole was repaired, and the following morning he lost twelve jars of pickled pigs feet. That was the last straw. He called the Sheriff who, in turn, called Jess Sweeten.

After talking to the grocer and examining the hole, Jess came up with a simple solution to the man's problem. One that would teach the thief a lesson he'd never forget.

Jess nailed about twenty fish hooks to a small plank then placed his trap on the shelf directly in front of the crack with the hooks facing foreword. If the thief tried to steal another can, he would be trapped.

Next morning, the grocer was surprised to learn that the trap had worked gruesomely well. He found shreds of torn shirt sleeve, a button and bloody chunks of skin that remained on twenty flattened fish hooks. A trail of blood leaving the scene of the crime proved the thief was badly in need of medical services.

A quick phone call to the local doctor was all he needed to identify the thief, and he was apprehended within an hour.

March 30, 1947
Jess Sweeten Wins State Shooting Competition With a Perfect Score at 25 Yards

THE MAN WHO LOVED SWEET POTATOES

Three quail hunters came across a funeral that was being held at the home of a backwoods farmer. The farm was located in a deep, wooded area southwest of Gun Barrel City.

The dead man had been dressed in his finest pair of overalls and placed in a hand-made wooden bier.

The coffin rested on two saw horses in the living room where the friends and relatives could view the body for one last time.

For some strange reason, the three hunters decided to play a sick joke on the unsuspecting crowd of mourners who were all gathered in the front yard.

They snuck up to the window and peeked inside to make sure the house was empty. It was! Everybody was in the front yard listening to the old country preacher who was preaching a powerful sermon of hope and love to the survivors of the dead man.

The hunters snuck around to the back of the house and eased in through the kitchen. The table was piled high with all kinds of food: hams, Sweet potatoes, black-eyed peas and corn bread. Collard greens were steaming on the wood cook-stove.

The hunters snickered to themselves as they eased into the living room without being noticed. They hefted the dead man out of the coffin then sat him upright on a large wooden rocker.

One of the hunters took a large bite out of a sweet potato then placed it carefully in the hand of the dear departed. All three escaped out the back door without being seen, then quickly disappeared in the thick underbrush behind the house.

On the following Sunday, the old preacher explained that what they had all witnessed at the farm was indeed a miracle of the meaning of true love. For a man so loved sweet potatoes, that he rose from the dead for one last bite.

After hearing about the miracle, Jess drove to Gun Barrel City to investigate. The preacher informed him that the miracle had indeed happened just the way he had heard it. He led the way to the miracle farm, and after a thirty minute search of the premises, Jess found three sets of footprints behind a large shrub fifty feet from the house. Apparently the hunters had watched the reaction of the mourners.

He returned to Gun Barrel City and arrested the three culprits who had made the mistake of bragging at the local filing station. They served three days in jail for malicious mischief.

ROOT HOG OR DIE

A coffee salesman named Bob Mckissack lived in Dallas, but he inherited the old home place north of Athens. It was a one-hundred-acre farm and two houses. The main house was a large Victorian, two-story home complete with a pillared front porch. It had a beautiful stone fireplace in the living room, with a chimney that serviced the three upper rooms.

The servant quarters was a nice four room house, roughly two hundred feet north of the main house. It also had a nice brick fireplace in the living room and a wood cook-stove in the kitchen. The farm had fifty head of livestock roaming a green pasture, and Bob drove to Athens on the weekend to care for his herd.

Soon he had built a large route of customers and didn't have time to care for the animals or the farm. Someone suggested that he find a family of renters for the servant quarters. They could take care of the whole place for free rent on the smaller house.

This man knew a family of people who would be proud to make such an arrangement.

Bob met the family on the following weekend and they struck a deal. The man and his family of twelve children promised to take real good care of the place for him, so Bob agreed to provide them a place to stay free of rent if the man met his obligation.

Bob would see them next spring.

The winter of 1931 was colder than hell with the furnace off, and snow covered the ground like grandma's quilt.

Bob began to worry about his cattle. Were they getting enough hay and sorghum molasses to see them through the cold winter? The renters swore they knew almost everything there was to know about cows, yet Bob couldn't wait until the roads cleared to have a look-see.

It was March of 1932 before he was able to make the trip.

He drove east to Wills Point on Highway 80, then turned south on Highway 64 to Canton, then turned right on highway 19. It was a pleasant drive but still pretty cold for that time of year. The sun was out, and he could enjoy the next seventeen miles of beautiful countryside.

Suddenly, he was inside the city limits of Athens. How did he pass the old home place without seeing it? He turned around and drove past the place again. *What in the world was going on?*

He turned around again. Finally he located the renters house; then the front gate to the large house. But the large house was gone. The whole damn house had disappeared.

The brick piers were there. The ground wasn't scorched so he knew it didn't burn down. The chimney and stone fireplace was there.

The mailbox was right there by the road. Right where it was supposed to be. The cows looked all right. All but two made it through the cold winter. All the furniture was piled around the shade-tree. He knew the renters were home because smoke was coming from the chimney, and the truck was parked in the yard.

Perhaps they could tell him what had happened.

He walked over to the rent house and they invited him right in. The old lady had a roast in the oven, and was stirring a caldron of beans like nothing was wrong.

"Where is my house?"

There was a long silence before a shame-faced, toe-headed kid spoke up. "We got real cold so pa' said we could use some of the planks from the porch. And before we knowed what happened, they wern't no more. Pa' said it was root hog or die."

"I want the lot of you out of here before noon!" Bob hollered.

"We can't leave until Grandma gets well."

"What's the matter with her?"

"She has a dose of the sickness."

Bob called Sheriff Baker, and Sheriff Baker called Jess. Within twenty minutes Jess pulled into the yard and noticed Grandma hanging clothes on the line. The old woman wasn't sick at all.

When Grandma saw Jess Sweeten get out of his patrol car, she quickly dropped an arm load of wet clothes and headed for the sick bed.

Jess told the family they had three hours to pack it up or he'd pack it for them.

"We ain't leaving 'till Grandma' gets well," said the renter.

"Then by damn she'll be out there in the highway!" said Sweeten.

Grandma was true to her word. She refused to budge. Jess was true to his word. He and another deputy named, Dallas Cramer toted grandma' and her sick bed out to the shoulder of the road and told her that she better get well quick or go to jail for obstructing traffic.

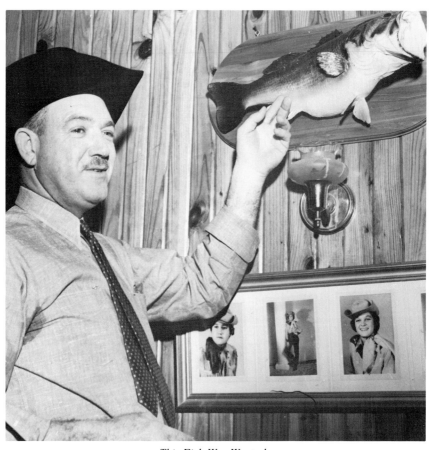

This Fish Was Wanted

THE SHOOT OUT IN CHANDLER

Charlie Fields, the constable of Chandler, had a problem with the Anderson Clan, and Roy Anderson in particular. They lived just east of town in an old frame house beside the highway. He was a lard-slick con artist, and a bully who had whipped nearly every man in town—but his specialty was stealing chickens. In general, Roy was a real nuisance to all the neighbors.

Charlie couldn't get through a single day without someone complaining about Roy Anderson. He pleaded with Roy to clean up his act, but with each visit to the Anderson home, Charlie was greeted with the business end of Roy's twelve gauge shotgun. After the fourth such visit, Charlie complained that Sheriff Baker should send re-enforcements to Chandler, Texas.

Sheriff Baker said the only solution to the Anderson problem was a good strong dose of Jess Sweeten. Baker ordered Jess to accompany Charlie Fields to Chandler and put an end to the Anderson problem. So that afternoon, Jess mapped a battle plan.

"You let me out in the woods about a quarter of a mile from the house," he told Charlie. "Then go to the door like you always do. I have a surprise for Mr. Anderson."

Charlie waited until Jess was in position before parking in the driveway. Jess took a position behind the house with his .30-30 rifle, and when the constable knocked on the door, Roy shoved the barrel of the shotgun in Charlie's teeth.

Charlie ran like a field mouse in the shadow of an eagle until he reached the opposite side of the house, then Roy fired. Charlie cleared a five-foot fence without touching timber, then dove head first behind the outhouse. Roy took a position behind the smoke house...with his back to Jess. It would have been an easy shot, but Jess held his fire.

"Throw down the gun," Jess shouted.

Anderson spun around, fired and missed, then dodged to the opposite corner of the smoke house, peering around the corner to get another shot. Jess took aim at that corner of the building just in front of the outlaw's eyes, firing round after round. Bullets whistled all around Roy's hiding place and splintered the wood into a thousand splinters, many of which stuck in Roy's face. Roy fell backward, dropping the shotgun—then Jess charged.

Jess continued firing all around Roy's ears, missing his face by inches. He emptied the rifle then fired out one of his forty-fives. "Don't move a damn muscle," He said calmly, easing to within three feet of the bad man. Suddenly one of Roy's brothers charged out the back door. Jess dropped him with a left hook. Within seconds, his sister ran out with a stick of stove wood cursing like a sailor. Jess turned her over his knee and gave her a spanking.

Jess Sweeten and Charlie Fields went through the Anderson house like a runaway locomotive—unearthing six more male Andersons armed with various types of artillery. At the end, nine of the Anderson clan were sitting in the Athens jail.

Roy was an army deserter, and was sent to Leavenworth prison, and Charlie Fields had no more trouble from the Anderson clan.

THE BOY SHERIFF OF HENDERSON COUNTY

No matter how small the crime everybody wanted Jess Sweeten to see about it. Reporters from three counties were now writing articles about the famous two-fisted young deputy, and according to the ladies, he was just plain purty.

Schoolgirls were showing up at the sheriff's office for autographs. Jess was hounded night and day by other law enforcement agencies who wanted shooting demonstrations for new recruits.

The Sheriff was fed up. People were treating Sheriff Baker as though he was Jess Sweeten's secretary. Baker felt he had no choice but to fire Jess after farmer called to report a stole cow. The farmer wanted Jess to take care of the matter personally.

Baker blew his top.

"I'm the damn sheriff around here!" he said. "If you have a problem...you call me about it!"

The farmer angrily shot back. "Joel! You might be the sheriff, but I want that thief caught!"

In his letter to Deputy Sweeten, Sheriff Joel Baker stated his feelings: "A deputy should never be more popular than the Sheriff." *Jess Sweeten was fired for being too popular.*

The decision of Sheriff Baker was final. Jess was free to seek employment elsewhere.

Baker's decision, however, caused an uproar throughout the county, and when the local newspaper learned the news, the following article appeared in the paper:

"Jess Sweeten, one of the most colorful officers in the history of Henderson County, passed out of the picture of local glamour this morning when he unbuckled his belt and placed his two guns on the table.

Sweeten tendered his resignation as Deputy Sheriff after receipt of a letter from Sheriff Joel Baker requesting him to do so. When asked for a reason Baker was noncommittal. Sweeten's last official act was to file charges of

drunkenness against three white men in Justice
Hall's court. He had made the arrests Sunday and
filed the charges just prior to giving up his
commission. It has been rumored for some time that Sweeten
would be asked to resign. In fact friends of the
deputy have been endeavoring to get him a
commission as a Ranger while others, on hearing
that he was to be let out on account of lack of
funds with which to pay him, had anticipated
raising his salary by public subscription. Admirers
of the deputy, on hearing of his resignation this
morning, were trying to get him on with some
other branch of law enforcement.
 Sweeten made quite a record as an officer at
Trinidad prior to coming to Athens. He succeeded in
quelling many disturbances in that little city
where others failed.
 On coming to Athens the first of the year, he
immediately began making arrests. Petitions were
sent from towns in the county asking that he be
sent to different communities.
 Tall handsome and of stately build, Sweeten
looks the part of the early day officers of Texas
and attracted a large following by the manner in
which he always "got his man."

After reading the article, Constable M. G. Jepsen of Athens hired
Jess as a deputy constable. The amount legally authorized for his salary
was no less than forty dollars per month so a petition was circulated
throughout the town's business section, and that amount was raised.
Deputy Constable, Jess Sweeten was assigned all Henderson County's
felony cases.

Jepsen had planned to run against Sheriff Baker in the next
election, so he asked Jess if he would toss his hat in the ring.

"That way," he said, "we can split Baker's votes, and if I win you
can have your old job back."

M. G. Jepsen lied.

He was not campaigning for himself; he was campaigning for Jess Sweeten. The only job Jepsen wanted was to be Jess' jailer and secretary.

Schoolgirls volunteered by handing out campaign literature. An ink blotter with his picture, and the words "JESS SWEETEN for

Check My Record---If I Have Made You a Good Sheriff I Will Appreciate Your Vote and Influence

JESS SWEETEN

Candidate For

SHERIFF

Henderson County (Re-election)

Subject to the Action of the Democratic Primaries

The only campaign literature Jess ever used.
Sold by school girls for $2.00 each

SHERIFF," but instead of giving the literature away, the girls were selling them for two dollars.

November, 2, 1932, the Athens Daily Review contained the results of the election:

> Jess Sweeten receives 2843 votes. Joel Baker receives 2091.
>
> ## JESS SWEETEN WINS BY 752 VOTES

Jess Sweeten was 24 years old at the time of the election. He was the youngest sheriff in the nation at the time. He appointed five deputies: Lee Wright, John Karnes, Calvin McWilliams, Dallas Cramer and M.G. Jepsen, who was selected for the job of jailer and secretary.

Jess' first duty was to raid a farm just north of Brownsboro, where a farmer was selling corn for a lot more than twenty-five cents a bushel. Although the farmer couldn't be found, they shot the still full of holes and destroyed fifty gallons of sour mash. The whiskey farmer salvaged the condensing worm, which meant a return visit.

The new job kept Jess going day and night, and chasing chicken thieves took so much time that he offered instructions on how to deal with the varmints: "First, kill the son of a bitch, then call the undertaker, then the magistrate for an inquest, and then call me." He further stated, that he didn't want to see another live chicken thief.

But that same morning while returning to his office, he noticed a black man running down the railroad tracks as fast as his legs could carry him—trailing a cloud of chicken feathers. He stopped at the crossing and noticed that the man was holding six chickens by the legs—three chickens in each hand. When the thief reached shouting distance, Jess hollered, "Where did you steal them damn chickens?"

The man slowed to a walk which offered time to think up a good story. Jess was anxious to hear it. Perhaps it was one he hadn't heard before.

"Mornin', Sheriff!"

"Mornin' hell! I asked where you where you stole them damn chickens!"

"These chickens?"

"Yes. Them damn chickens!"

Mr. Jess, I didn't steal these chickens. These chickens is a friend of mine's chickens."

"What the hell are you doing with 'em?"

"Mr. Jess, it was the funniest thang. I wuz down there seeing him on a visit, and when I left, they jus' commence to foller me home. I shoos em' this-a-way and I shoos em' that-a-way, but dem little devils jis' kept a coming."

Jess interrupted. "And they got tired of walking so you decided to carry 'em a while?"

"I'z scared a train might come along and run 'em over, so I ponders what to do about it, and then figures I could maybe jis' take 'em back in the mornin'!"

A small pile of corn began forming near the man's bare foot but he quickly covered it with his left, hopefully in time to conceal the fact that the chickens had been lured away from their owner.

Jess couldn't help but notice how thin and frail the man looked. *He could hide behind a clothesline pole.* Jess thought to himself. *The poor som-bitch needed them damn chickens.* Jess nodded and said, "Can I count on that?"

"Yes, suh!...first thang in the morning."

"One more thing" Jess said. " Tell your wife to sew up that pocket. You're losing all your bait."

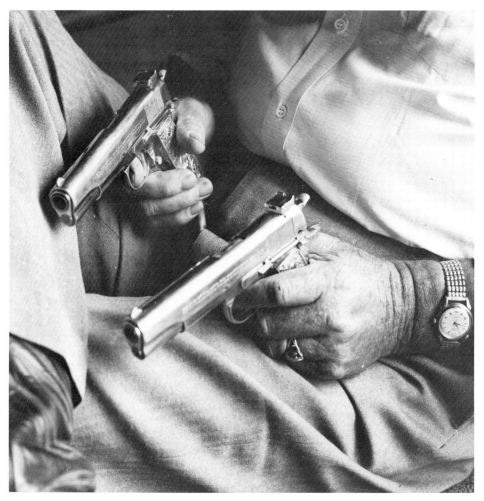

Sweeten's Famous Matched Colt .45 Pistols

AMOS DODD

It was January 1933. The country was broke; the state was broke; the county and cities were broke, and Amos Dodd was broke. First his job at the sawmill played out, then the money and friends ran out. And it wasn't long until the food ran out.

Amos was not a thief. He did what any man would do under the same circumstances, because a man can't stand by and watch his family go hungry. So he boxed up five dollars' worth of groceries at the Piggly Wiggly, and walked out without paying.

Jess was summoned by the irate store owner who wanted the man arrested. The grocer was having a hard time paying the wholesaler due to all the unpaid tickets of his customers, and Amos was already fifty-five dollars in arrears before he absconded with the last bill of groceries.

"After all I've done for that man," the grocer said, "you'd think he'd at least ask. But no, he lit out of here like a buck-shot coyote."

Jess promised to talk to the man, and within minutes, found him sitting on his front porch. Amos expected the visit and offered to go quietly, but Jess noticed eight sets of hungry little eyes peering through the screened front door and windows, and they watched his every move. If he was going to arrest Amos, he'd be the enemy of every one of those kids—and they'd remember this day for the rest of their lives. Jess knew that it was important to treat a man with dignity, especially in front of his children, or the man would loose a measurable amount of respect from his family. So he decided to take a friendly approach. He stepped onto the porch with a large smile, shook hands with Amos and said, "How are you doing Mr. Dodd?"

Amos noticed the children at the window so he spoke very quietly, "Sheriff, I know why you're here and I'm ready to go. I just want you to know one thing. I'm not a thief. I know that what I did wrong but I just didn't know what else to do."

Jess offered Amos a cigarette then walked with him to the side of the house where the family couldn't hear what was said. "Amos, you're not going to jail, so don't worry about that. But we do have to figure a way out of this mess. I've talked to Mr. Weaver and he's pretty upset. The poor fellow owes his supplier a world of money and they're hounding him to death for it. And if he can't pay up...well, he has a family too."

Jess lit a match on his thumbnail then cupped his hands and offered Amos a light. "Look," he said, "I'm going to pay for the groceries. It's a loan, until you get on your feet. I'll tell Mr. Weaver you had a lot on your mind and just forgot to pay him. That way you can face the man without feeling like a thief."

Tears ran down Amos' face as Jess walked toward the Buick. He stood silently for a moment then suddenly rushed to the car before Jess could back out of the driveway.

"Sheriff!" he shouted, "My wife makes good biscuits, and we'd appreciate if you'd join us."

Jess smiled then quickly killed the engine and said, "Well, it's been a long time since I had a good biscuit." He knew it would be disrespectful to turn down such an offer, so he accepted, and Amos was right, she did make good biscuits.

THE PEOPLES LAWMAN

The job of county sheriff paid three hundred dollars a month if the check didn't bounce, and most of the time they bounced two or three times before they were cleared. Somehow, half Jess' salary found it's way into po-folks' pockets, and in those days, Henderson County was populated by a lot of po-folks.

Politicians, however, fared pretty well in those tough times. When a farm went on the auction block, the first one to know about it was the politician, and many were eager to pick them up for taxes. This annoyed Jess more than any single duty. Any man with half a conscience would dread the job of forcing a good family off their farm. Elected officials did most of the buying, but after a few threats, Jess won a resolution which would make it unlawful for a public trustee to bid on seized property.

Jess also started a bank for children after many were caught stealing cookies, empty coke bottles, or small amounts of money from the local merchants. He asked the county for two hundred dollars in small change so the children could go to the picture show, buy an ice cream cone or a soda water. All a child had to do was fill out the necessary paperwork, and the money would be given them. There was one provision: The money had to be repaid before they could borrow more. Jess' special bank became very popular with the kids of Athens because it taught responsibility—and it showed that the law was a friend. When Jess retired some twenty years later the money was counted for the final time, and the total came to two hundred dollars. All loans made by the kids had been repaid—a record unmatched by any regular grown-up bank.

Jess and His Bull

HAZEL POTTER

Three months after becoming Sheriff, Jess began dating a young eighteen-year-old girl named Hazel Potter. She was one of the schoolgirls who had helped distribute the campaign literature. Her father, Horace Potter forbade her to date Jess, citing the fact that he was now twenty-six years old.

Hazel said that his decision made no sense. Her daddy had not voted for Jess because he was too young. She continued an unrelenting barrage of "why-not's," and pestered the poor man night and day. She loved Jess Sweeten, and if only he would talk to him she bet that he would like him also.

"Hazel, the man's twenty-six years old!"

"Just talk to him. That's all I ask!" Hazel continued.

"I won't hear any more about it!" he said.

"Please. Just talk to him for a few minutes." she begged.

"No!""Pretty please."

"Baby, I said no."

She kissed him on the forehead. "Pretty please with sugar on it."

"Baby."

He was wearing down. Now for the kill. "Daddy, I love you. Please talk to him."

"Alright. I'll talk to him. He's got one hour, and that's all."

Jess was invited to the Potter house for the first time that Friday night and both men were somewhat nervous about meeting each other. Jess was nervous because he knew Hazel had to beg her daddy to meet with him. Mr. Potter in turn, had read all the stories about Jess in the paper. And from what he had read, he figured Jess to be a rough and rowdy, hell-bent-for-leather sort of fellow. Instead, he found Jess to be quite the opposite.

Jess was very articulate in his speech, and his quiet calm manner was refreshing. He'd do to ride the river with.

The two men talked during supper, they talked after supper, they talked in the living room, they talked on the front porch, they talked until Hazel bade both a goodnight. They continued talking until three o'clock in the morning.

Jess and Hazel were married six months after he had been elected Sheriff. They spent their honeymoon at the fancy Adolphus hotel in Dallas, Texas. When they arrived, the desk clerk handed Jess the keys to the Governor's Suite -which was way up on the top floor.

It was the finest suite of rooms in Dallas and had a breathtaking the view of the downtown area. The hotel offered twenty-four hour room service, flowers and a large basket of fruit arrived each morning. The Adolphus flaunted every comfort. Budweiser and Adolphus Coors had built a marvelous hotel on the northwest corner of Commerce and Akard streets. The building replaced the old Gothic City Hall in 1913. The roof above the Governor's Suite was an elaborately decorated Beaux-Arts design, complete with a copper-capped, beer-bottle turret. A truly majestic structure indeed, but Jess noticed something the Adolphus Hotel did not have. A fire escape.

The thought of such a structure catching fire was beginning to worry the living daylights out of Jess. *What if it caught fire way down there on the third floor*, he thought to himself. *Why, they'd fry like cracklings.*

And to top that, he looked inside the hand carved chest-of-drawers and found a card that read:

"Governor's Suite, $50.00 per day!"

Fifty dollars a day! he thought, *that's three hundred and fifty dollars!...*That's a months pay!

He didn't want Hazel to be upset, but he didn't have anywhere near that much money. With meals costing a full day's wages and the souvenirs that Hazel wanted, he'd have to sneak off to Athens and borrow some money from the bank. Sleep would be impossible until he could figure a way out of this mess. If the thing caught fire during the middle of the night, both he and Hazel could kiss this old world good-bye.

He spoke to the hotel manager about the problem, but the slick-haired fellow told him the place was pretty near fireproof. As far as Jess was concerned, *pretty near* didn't solve the problem.

Hazel was quick to agree that the man was more-than-likely right since he worked there. She tried to assure Jess that it was not going to catch on fire, and he shouldn't be all that worried about it.

"Sugar, not only is it possible, it's very likely. And before this thing burns to the ground with us in it, I'm going to find us a way out of here."

It was unimaginable to Jess why anyone would spend so much money to build such a fine place, and not spend a single dime to save a life. So when Hazel went shopping for dust collectors, he did a bit of surveying outside the building. He counted the floors and figured the distance from the top to bottom at approximately three hundred feet. Late that afternoon he walked into the lobby dragging three hundred feet of rope. He had himself a home-made fire escape.

The manager's face flushed cotton-pale. Guests were in the lobby. Well-dressed out-of-town guests, and Jess was dragging a huge pile of rope toward the elevator. People were looking—wondering what in the world was going on.

The manager rushed to the elevator as Jess pushed the button. "Sir, is there something wrong?" he asked. Jess backed inside the elevator which was pretty well loaded with distinguished gentlemen guests and their lady friends. Jess smiled politely as he tipped his hat, then stuffed the rope in the front corner of the fancy elevator and said, "No! Everything is just fine now, thank you!"

Jess and Hazel remained at the Adolphus hotel for the remainder of the week. On the morning of the last day, he asked the desk clerk how much they had spent so far. Hazel was off visiting with the wife of the Dallas County sheriff, and Jess had planned to secretly drive to the Athens bank without her knowing.

"Why, Mr. Sweeten, your room has been paid in full."

"Well, who paid for it?" Jess asked in amazement.

"Sir, I'm not allowed to tell you that."

It was never learned who paid, but the gift was never forgotten.

SON BEULAH

When Jess and Hazel returned to Athens they were greeted by several deputies and a reporter from the newspaper. The county provided the newlyweds a small, rent-free apartment inside the jail where Jess could be reached night or day.

Chief Deputy Dallas Cramer was unloading the luggage from the trunk when he spotted the large coil of rope. He laughed and said, "Jess we knew you and Hazel were tying the knot, but I sure as heck didn't know it would take that much rope."

Before Jess could answer, a prisoner on the second floor stuck his head out the second floor window and yelled: "Sheriff! When is that cook gonna' snap on the feed bag?"

Jess looked at his watch. It was one thirty. "Hazel, would you go in there and see what's taking her so long. They should have been fed an hour ago."

Hazel casually walked into the kitchen and was greeted with the shock of her life. The back door was standing wide open, and the kitchen was a mess. The smell of burned beans filled the room. The screen was torn off the back door. Bits of salt pork and broken dishes covered the floor. And behind the overturned table, and something worse—Roena, the jail cook was lying in a pool of blood.

Hazel had promised the girl a job before she and Jess married. She was a young, pretty twenty-two-year-old Negro girl, and a good cook. Now she lay motionless on the floor. Both her eyes were swelled shut. Her clothes were torn away from her breasts. Fleshy skin from the inside of her mouth was hanging loosely from the corner of her swelled bottom lip.

Hazel's scream brought Jess crashing thru the door with his forty-five automatic cocked, aimed and ready. Hazel placed a towel under Roena's head, then began to wipe her face with a wet dish rag. Seconds later, Roena awakened and tried to get to her feet. "Stay where you are Roena," Jess said as his face reddened with anger. "What happened, Roena?" Jess asked.

She began whimpering, which was a good sign. "I'm alright sheriff." She tried to spit the stringy skin from her mouth. "I got to get the dinner ready."

Jess repeated. "Dammit, girl, who did this to you?"

Hazel wiped tears from Roena's eyes then asked softly, "Did Son Beulah do this, Roena?"

Hazel knew that Son Beulah had been pestering Roena for several months. Hazel wanted to tell Jess but Roena said it was nothing to worry Jess about. She was afraid that Jess would put Beulah in jail and that would make it worse.

Roena began to cry, nodding her head. "He just won't leave me alone."

Son Beulah had followed Roena to work that Sunday morning, and stood at the back of the jail for two hours, watching her through the screen door. She had rejected Son Beulah's advances. He was very angry that she was dating a skinny undertaker's son.

Roena stood at the kitchen sink with her back to the door and had not noticed the big black ease the door open. Cooking noises and her singing had hidden his steps toward her. Then, with one swift motion, he spun her around, kissed her forcefully while pressing her tightly to his chest.

Beulah half carried Roena to the kitchen table, then forced her, face down, on the red checkered table cloth. When she attempted to scream, her arms were twisted high behind her back, causing excruciating pain.

With one hand, Son Beulah unbuttoned his trousers and let them fall to the floor. He lifted Roena's dress with the same hand while holding her left arm with the other. He forced himself between her legs, released both arms then positioned both of his massive arms around her waist; threatening to kill her if she moved or made a sound.

When he released his grip on her left arm, she slowly reached for the handle of a heavy cast-iron skillet with her right. Then with one swift motion she swung the skillet backward toward Son Beulah's head.

She heard a loud thump. The skillet found its mark. Son Beulah staggered backward and covered his face with his hands. Blood trickled from the huge knot on his forehead and down his nose.

She ran bravely toward him, cursing, yelling and swinging the skillet with all her mite. Again the skillet found its mark, sending Son Beulah crashing through the screen door.

With hands wringing wet and a mouth dry as cotton, she ran to the water faucet. All she could think of now was a cool drink of water. Her stomach churned. She was weeping in short moaning jerks then suddenly she regurgitated her breakfast in the sink. It was her last memory until she heard Hazel screaming for Jess.

Jess noticed Dallas standing in the doorway with his pistol drawn.

"Call Doc Henderson!" Jess ordered, then ejected the clip of the forty-five into his left hand. He gave it a quick glance, then pressed the top shell. The clip was full. He walked toward the door looking sternly toward Dallas Cramer.

"And tell Doc Henderson that he's going to have the busiest day of his life. You tell him that!!" He continued out the doorway mumbling angrily to himself. "By God, he'll never touch you again! That's for sure! That's for damn sure!"

As a deputy, Jess had arrested Beulah several times. The man was easily identified by his narrow deep set eyes that had a tint of yellow. He stood roughly six-foot-two inches tall, and weighed approximately two hundred and forty pounds.

Son Beulah's hangout was the Negro store in the Freedman section. It was an old weather-worn unpainted building with a covered porch. A number of sheet metal signs advertising soft drinks, snuff and Old Gold Cigarettes hung on the walls and posts.

Several blacks were playing horseshoes beside the building while Son Beulah and three other men played dominoes under the large oak to the right the front porch.

Son Beulah placed a domino on the spinner then yelled, "Gimmie that damn nickel!"

A skinny black named Jabo Windfield rubbed his chin, pondering his next play. Another black playfully slapped Jabo on the head and told him to hurry up. Jabo placed a domino on the wrong spinner and quickly marked an X on the tablet. "Gimmie a dime!" Son Beulah slapped him on the head, much harder than the other black, causing Jabo to fall off the stool.

"Yo' butt git's a damn dime!" said Beulah. "Nigger, if you don't know how to play, git' ye' nappy ass out the game!!"

Another black laughed and removed the domino.

"Hell, it ain't his fault, Calvin. Dat' damn dennis' pulled da' nigger's wisdom teeth...Po' nigger been dumb as hell ever' since."

A cloud of red road-dust was being kicked up by the sheriff's big Buick. Jabo Windfield figured that dust had something to do with the huge knot on Son Beulah's head. It was time for him to get a soda water.

Jess slid to a stop directly in front of the store. The huge dust cloud took a full thirty seconds to expose the angry face of Jess Sweeten standing on the running board with a forty-five automatic aimed at Son Beulah.

"Now I'm going to shoot ONE rat!" Jess shouted.

People scattered. One ran behind the large oak near the corner of the store. Some ran behind the store and others seemed to disappear in thin air—all except Calvin Williams, alias Son Beulah. He stood defiantly.

Jess stepped off the running board and walked toward Son Beulah with a slow and steady gate. Son Beulah stepped from behind the domino table as if ready to fight. Jess fired one shot which tore into Beulah's leg just above the knee. He took four more steps toward Williams and fired again. The second shot splattered Beulah's hand. Three more steps and Sweeten fired again, striking Beulah's shoulder.

Son Beulah dropped to the ground and covered his eyes with his right arm. Son Beulah was expecting the final shot. When it didn't come he chanced a peek and noticed the barrel of Jess' forty-five aimed directly between his eyes.

"Don't shoot me no more." he pleaded in a whisper.

"What did you say?" Jess hollered.

"Please don't shoot me no more," he said, this time with a louder voice.

"I can't hear you, Calvin!" Jess shouted louder.

Please don't shoot me no more Mr. Jess! Beulah screamed at the top of his lungs.

Jess eased the hammer down.

"Then crawl to that car!...On all fours, damn you! like an animal! That's what you are...A dammed animal!"

He loaded Calvin Williams in the trunk of the car and rushed him to the jail, where Dr. Henderson stopped the bleeding in the nick of time.

Dallas Cramer noticed the condition of Jess' prisoner and asked whether the man was going to live or not. Jess gave him an icy glance then said, "Yeah, he'll live. But, by damn he'll not do it in my county–!

Three months later, a plot to murder Jess Sweeten was planned by Son Beulah and his two friends, Jabbo Winfield and Manvel Dawson.

Son Beulah wanted Jess dead for gunning him down like a dog. Manvel Dawson wanted Jess dead because he had been fired as the jail janitor after he had caught the syphilis. Jabbo Winfield wanted Jess dead because he destroyed a truckload of his good drinking whiskey.

The men met at the home of Manvel Dawson. Manvel was to go to the jail and tell the sheriff there was some trouble at the Royall Cotton Gin. Son Beulah and Jabbo Winfield would be waiting behind two oil drums and would come up shooting when Manvel whistled.

Manvel ran excitedly to the jail and said, "I need to see Mr. Jess about the trouble at the cotton gin!"

"What kind of trouble?" Deputy Homer Williams asked.

"I got to tell Mr. Jess personal!" he said.

"Well, Mr. Jess and Dallas Cramer are out of town for a week. I'm in charge of all the trouble until they get back. What kind of trouble are you talking about?"

The Negro seemed disappointed and began to stammer.

"Well, suh'...It ain't big trouble. It's just little trouble. It's the kind of trouble what can wait till Mr. Jess come back."

Homer began to get highly suspicious, so, after Manvel left, he called Charlie Fields, the new city marshall. He and Charlie waited until dark, then eavesdropped through Manvel's open window. When they heard the new plan, both charged in for the arrest. Manvel and Jabbo were caught; Son Beulah escaped out the back door.

Jabbo and Manvel were brought to court and charged with conspiracy to commit murder. The bail was set at two thousand dollars each. Manvell pleaded, "Mr. Homer, we wuz was just gonna shoot Mr. Jess a little bit; not a whole lot. The Judge, he set the bail way to high for that kind of shootin'."

Son Beulah was killed by the husband of his girl friend three days after he returned to Palestine.

Jess and His Horse "Dan"

THE EUSTACE BANK ROBBERY

"Sheriff, this is the first National Bank in Eustace. We've just been robbed of thirty-eight hundred dollars!"

Jess quickly wrote a description of the two robbers on a sheet of paper and had secretary M. G. Jepsen immediately telephone the sheriffs of all adjoining counties. Then he jumped into his car and sped toward the Eustace bank to investigate.

On his arrival at the bank, He was told that two men, armed with revolvers, had entered the bank and ordered everybody to put their hands in the air.

A bank employee described one of the two as being in his early twenties, roughly five feet ten inches in height, and weighing about a hundred and fifty pounds. The younger man wore a mask which was crudely fashioned with black adhesive tape.

Jess was questioning the bank employees, when a man came rushing in and asked, "Is it true the bank was robbed?"

"Yes. Two men stuck it up! Why?"

"Well, I think I saw them!"

"What makes you think it was them? Did they do something to make you suspicious?"

"Yes, sir, I saw two men running from the direction of the bank!"

"Which way did they go?"

"They ran about a block, then jumped into a 1931, black four-door Chevrolet, and it didn't have a license plate. The right rear window was cracked and held together by several strips of tape."

"What direction did they take out of town?"

"Right down there. Toward Malakoff."

"I appreciate the information," said the sheriff.

Jess and his deputies returned to his office in Athens, then began working desperately trying to get leads when a lady from Malakoff called his office. Jess answered the phone.

"Sheriff, if you'll come down to Malakoff I may have some information for you on that bank robbery."

That evening Jess drove to the lady's bungalow near the center of town. Although it had not yet begun to rain, clouds were forming. They were, dark, heavy rain clouds. The kind that make deep gullies in all the country roads.

"Sheriff, I'm a married woman, and what I have to tell you must be kept a secret. My husband is out of town so this gave me the opportunity to talk to you. Did one of those robbers have a strip of tape on his face?"

"Yes, he did. Why?"

"Well, I've been having an affair with a man from Tennessee Colony. He came to see me last night wearing a strip of tape on the right side of his jaw."

"What's his name?"

"Emmit Pettit. I asked him why he was wearing the tape, and he told me he had gone to a dance the night before. He said he got in an fight with a man who cut him with a pocket knife."

"Well, ma'am. The one I'm looking for, had about seventy-five percent of his face covered with tape."

"Well, then I guess my information won't help."

Jess thanked the woman then drove away. Although, he made it a point to remember the name of the woman's lover. Sometimes the slightest, most insignificant scrap of information could be the one that breaks the case.

Night fell rapidly, and the rain had become a frog-strangler.

When he arrived back in Athens, he picked up a couple of deputies. The rain was really pouring now, and the roads were terrible. But he wanted to be in Tennessee colony before all the bridges washed out. Suddenly, about a half mile from town, one of his deputies spotted a 1931 Chevrolet which was identical in every detail with the robbers' car. It had the cracked right rear window which was patched with black adhesive tape!

Jess got out of the car then knocked on the door of the house where the car was parked in the driveway; but only after placing his deputies at strategic points behind the house. There was no answer, but he could hear muffled sounds coming from the front bedroom.

Sweeten aimed the beam of his flashlight through the window and noticed a man and woman on the bed. The woman had pulled the covers over her head, and the man was sitting on the side of the bed with a .45 automatic in his hands.

Jess shouted through the window, "I'm Sheriff Sweeten from Athens. I just want to ask a few questions."

"Don't you go out there," the woman warned, "you don't know who those people are."

"How do I know you're a sheriff!" the man shouted back, releasing the safety of his automatic.

"Well, If you'll come to the damn door I'll identify myself."

For a few moments Jess thought the fellow might cause trouble. The man's hesitation seemed to be even more suspicious.

"I'm not going to stand out here in the damn rain all night fellow! You're surrounded. And if you're thinking of trying something, By damn, you won't stand a chance!. Now you come on out of there!"

The man laid his gun on the floor then came to the door. He opened the door just wide enough to scan one eye toward the large wet stranger on the porch. Jess showed him the badge, and the man, in return, said that he was a sewing machine salesman. He asked the sheriff to step inside out of the rain. He quickly became very co-operative. Sheriff Sweeten stepped inside the door after the salesman turned on the light.

"Where were you at about two-thirty this afternoon?"

"I was in Palestine at 3:00 o'clock" he said, then produced a receipt which indicated that he had sold some chickens at a poultry house in Palestine.

"I take chickens in payment when I can't get money. Then I take them over to Palestine and sell them. Folks are a little short on cash these days," the salesman grinned.

Since he had been in Palestine at three o'clock and it was near forty-five miles from Eustace, it was illogical to suspect that this man had anything to do with the robbery since it happened at 2:00 p.m.

"Sheriff, now you have my curiosity aroused. What brings you out on a night like this?"

"I am working on a robbery case that was committed in my county this afternoon. Your car fit the description of the get-a-way car. Do you know anyone in this neighborhood that has a car like yours? With tape on the back right window."

"Emmit Pettit has a car just like mine. He lives about a mile down the road. It's just like mine, same model, same color, broken glass and everything. Tape and all."

There's Emmit Pettit's name again, Jess thought to himself. Now he didn't feel so bad about disturbing the salesman at that hour of the night. He called the deputies from behind the house, apologized to the man for having intruded on his rest, then headed for the Pettit home.

When they arrived, neither Emmit nor his car was there. They continued on to Palestine, to enlist the aid of Sheriff Macklin. *The suspects, more-than-likely, were all from Anderson County,* thought Jess. And therefore, he must inform the Anderson County sheriff. Sheriff Macklin agreed to help and co-operate in every way possible. About daylight the next morning, they returned to Pettit's home in Tennessee Colony. He was a rough character who had a string of arrests for minor offenses. Luck was with them. Pettit's 1931 Chevrolet sedan with it's broken rear window was parked in the driveway.

Pettit was at home!

He offered no resistance, but he had a swaggering, cocky attitude about being awakened at that early hour. At the time of his arrest, he was still wearing the strip of tape on the right side of his jaw covering the alleged cut on his chin.

Dr. Henderson, the county coroner and jail physician, examined Pettit and found that he did indeed have a gash on his chin made by a sharp instrument. After the examination, he drove the prisoner to the First National Bank in Eustace. Deputy Elton Corley drove the suspect's car.

Jess entered the bank alone. He told the bank employees to try to identify his prisoner, but asked them not to say anything in front of the man when he brought him in. A few minutes later, he would return by himself, and they would be free to speak their mind. He then stepped out and came back with Emmit Pettit.

All the employees agreed that Pettit was not one of the robbers. The man did not in the least, resemble either of the two thieves. The next man to try to identify Petit was the man who said he had seen the get-a-way-car. But after looking the car over, he said:

"Sheriff, I don't know if that's the car or not. It looks like it. But this one has a license plate. The other car didn't have no license plate. However, it's got the same cracked window and all!"

Deputy Corley shook his head in disbelief, "Jess," he snickered, "sometimes a fella can follow a good lead right down a blind alley."

While driving back to Athens, Jess had a strong feeling which caused him to believe he had the right man. He felt that Emmit had indeed taken part in the crime. And was more-than-likely, the driver of the get-a-way car. But how many cars were going to show up with a cracked rear window which had been repaired with adhesive tape, he had found two himself. Even though the bank employees had failed to identify Pettit, and though the get-a-way car was only partially identified, he felt it was enough to lodge Mr. Pettit in the Henderson County jail.

About this time, Chief deputy Dallas Cramer walked in.

"Jess, what's our next move?"

"Call the other two deputies in," he said, "I want to talk to all of you." Sweeten addressed his deputies: "Men, we're going to stay with this thing until we get it solved. We have one suspect in jail, but we don't have one particle of evidence against him. Now, we can't hold him long without charges being filed, and we don't have enough evidence to file charges. Any minute, some damn lawyer is going to walk in here with a habeas corpus and we'll have to let him go. But, I'm convinced that Pettit was the driver."

Painstakingly, they reviewed the case step by step. He drew a wide arc across the Henderson County map with his thumb and finger.

"Somewhere between these two points, Eustace and Tennessee Colony, a distance of thirty-five miles, somebody saw that Chevrolet sedan. My reason is this. The weather conditions on that day were, to say the least, out of the ordinary if not exceptional. In other words, those roads were muddy as hell. The traffic in those conditions would be just about nil. Therefore, we ought to be able to find someone that noticed the car. And if we do, he might be able to identify Pettit."

There were no less than twenty back roads between Eustace and Tennessee Colony, and that meant leg work, lots of leg work. Through mud lanes and washed-out wagon-ruts in hopes of finding the proverbial needle in a hay stack. But the only way to solve any crime required determination and tenacity. This was the only formula since there were no solid leads or clues with which Sweeten could pin his hopes.

The first thirty miles of constant effort were to no avail. They produced nothing in the way of evidence. Each man had his individually assigned strip of roads to prevent overlapping, and they stopped for neither food, rest, nor drink. They kept plodding on.

Late in the afternoon, about four o'clock, Dallas Cramer came driving down the road and pulled up alongside Sheriff Sweeten.

"Sheriff, I think I've hit pay dirt! I want you to come with me and hear a man's story."

Sweeten parked his car and Cramer drove him to an old run down farmhouse. The farmer greeted the sheriff and asked, "Sheriff, Will you hold everything I say in strict confidence?"

"I can't promise that because I may have to subpoena you as a witness. But if you have any information that will be helpful I want it," explained the sheriff.

"Sheriff, they could burn my barn, shoot my cows or hurt my family if I get mixed up in this."

Jess promised, "Look, if there is any way in the world to try this case without your testimony, then I'll keep your information a secret."

With evidence of relief the farmer said, "Yes. I saw Emmit Pettit on this road. He was headed south. I was down the road south of here feeding my cows. When I started back to the house, I saw Pettit and two other men in Pettit's car. Emmit was driving. He was slipping and sliding all over the road. For a minute there, I thought he'd end up in the ditch. So I pulled over to the side as far as I could so he could get around me."

"Did you recognize the other two men?"

"Sure!"

"Who were they?"

"It was Howard Wingate and Lindsey Williams."

Jess reflected a moment. The name Williams didn't ring a bell, but Wingate did.

"What time of day was that?"

"It was four o'clock last Monday afternoon."

At least, these few scraps of information began to make sense. The bank was held up at two-thirty. The intervening hour and a half would have given them just enough time to reach the farmer's house at four o'clock. Due to the road conditions, it would have taken them at least that long.

The sheriff and his men thanked the farmer then drove back to Athens.

That night he and one of his deputies returned to Palestine, to the home of twenty-two-year-old Lindsey Williams, having first enlisted the aid of Sheriff Macklin.

Williams was arrested then placed in the Henderson County jail at Athens. Williams was from a well respected family in Palestine.

Williams connection with the bank robbery came as a surprise to Sweeten. He was questioned at length that night by Jess and his three deputies. He admitted nothing! He said that he had nothing to do with the robbery in any form or fashion.

Jess and his men retired for some badly needed rest because they had been on the go for three days and nights. But early the next morning they all met at the jail office.

"Well, we have two suspects in jail, and the evidence is still pretty slim." Jess looked at his watch then continued, "It's about an hour before the bank opens in Eustace. So here's the plan for today: Cramer, you and I are going to deliver Mr. Williams over to the bank when it opens. Hopefully, we'll get an identification."

He turned to Deputy Elton Corley: "Corley, Lindsey Williams works for the railroad over in Palestine, so you head over there and check his time card. We'll need that card as evidence if it shows he didn't show up for work last Monday. When you find out, meet me back here."

Cramer and Sweeten delivered Williams to the Eustace bank just as it opened at 9:30 a.m. The entire bank personnel identified Williams as one of the robbers. One lady employee said, "Why that is the man who wore the tape on his face and held the gun while on us while the other bandit went behind the counter and scooped up all the money!"

Williams was returned to the Athens jail.

Although Jess was reasonably sure of the suspect's guilt, he still did not have enough evidence to take to the grand jury. Meanwhile, Corley had returned from Palestine.

"The time card," said Corley, "shows that Williams checked in for work at 8:30 a.m. on Monday morning, but he checked out an hour and a half later at 9:30 a.m. on the day of the robbery!"

The evidence began to pile up against Williams.

Jess thought that with the identification at the bank and the incriminating time card, he might be able to get a confession from Lindsey Williams. This, however was wishful thinking. He and the deputies questioned Williams the entire day without results. He doggedly insisted that the witnesses were mistaken in their identification.

But late that afternoon Williams' mother walked into the sheriff's office and introduced herself. She was a hard-as-nails east Texas woman who had just about enough of her wayward son.

"Sheriff, are holding my boy, Lindsey Williams for bank robbery?"

"Yes, Mrs. Williams, it is true."

Sheriff Sweeten went on to explain that her son had been positively identified by all bank employees. He told Mrs. Williams that her son's time card showed that he left work at 9:30 a.m. on the day of the bank holdup, and that his foreman told a deputy, Lindsey had left work because of a severe cold.

"Your son, however, denies that he had anything to do with the robbery."

Suddenly, Mrs. Williams shocked everyone.

"Sheriff, I believe he's as guilty as he can be...May I talk with him?"

"Yes, Mrs. Williams, you may."

Accompanied by Jess and two deputies, Mrs. Williams was taken to the second floor to her son's cell where he was being held incommunicado. The jailer unlocked the door to Williams' cell.

"Lindsey Williams, what are you doing in this jail?"

"Mother, it looks like they're trying to file bank robbery charges against me," he replied meekly.

Mrs. Williams angrily pointed her finger at her son and said, "Lindsey, you are as guilty as hell and you know it!"

She continued her accusations.

"Up until now, you have never given your daddy and me any trouble. But, I've warned you against the type of company you have been keeping for the past few weeks." She sat down wearily on a bunk next to her son and looked him straight in the eye. Her voice had toned down quite a bit.

"Lindsey, if you continue this lying I'm going to let you rot in this jail house. Because that will prove to me and your daddy that you don't want to do right. But, since you've never given us any trouble before, we'll give you a chance if you promise to straighten up and fly right. We'll get a good lawyer and fight this thing through."

The candid appeal made by Williams' mother was overpowering. He broke down and confessed everything to his mother, implicating Emmit Pettit as the driver of the get-a-way car and Howard Wingate and himself as the two who held up the bank.

In his career as a peace officer, Sheriff Sweeten had never before had a mother assist in wringing a confession from her son.

76

"She is to be highly commended for the attitude she took," said Jess sincerely.

Lindsey offered to show where his third of the bank robbery money was hidden. He was taken from jail and directed the officers to his home in Anderson County about thirty miles south of Athens.

Lindsey got out of the sheriff's car and walked to a fence. He pulled out a fence post then laid it on the ground, reached inside the post hole and came up with a half-gallon fruit jar filled with the loot.

Williams was again returned to the Henderson County jail where he awaited the filing of bank robbery charges and arraignments. Chief Deputy Cramer, Deputy Corley, and Sheriff Sweeten headed for the last member of the Eustace bank robbery trio.

Jess warned his deputies, "Running down Wingate may not be an easy job. He's a seasoned criminal and a bank robber. He has robbed two banks that I know of, and maybe three."

Wingate's house set back in the foot of the mountains east of Montalba, a small town in Anderson County. Jess placed Cramer and Corley on each side of Wingate's house while he went to the front door and knocked. Howard's mother, Mrs. Wingate, came to the door. She appeared very nervous.

Mrs. Wingate, I'm Sheriff Sweeten from Athens. Where is Howard, Mrs. Wingate?"

"Why he's down at the McCormick house in Brushy Creek community, near the Brushy Creek school."

"Thank you, ma'am."

The three lawmen left the Wingate house then drove to Palestine. They picked up Sheriff Macklin, and one of his deputies then proceeded to the McCormick house.

When Howard Wingate learned that his two partners had been captured, he swore not to be taken alive. It was reported that Wingate was heavily armed, and wouldn't hesitate to come out shooting.

The lawmen approached the McCormick house with Jess and Sheriff Macklin in the lead car. It was dark as pitch, and the rains continued. Jess turned his lights off then proceeded up the long driveway toward the front yard. The other cars, with their lights out, stopped directly behind Jess and Macklin.

Jess and Macklin eased to the front porch with shotguns ready. Macklin moved to the opposite side of the door and stepped on a loose plank. A light came on in a bedroom to the right of a long hallway, and a half-naked man ran scrambled down the hall, pulling his trousers up as he ran out the back door. Jess ran around the house followed by several deputies. As Jess turned the corner near the back door, the suspect turned the opposite direction and ran through a cordon of deputies who began firing at the suspect.

"Stop! This is the Sheriff!" Jess shouted, as the man continued toward high weeds at the edge of the back yard. Jess aimed, warned the man again, then fired the shotgun. Lint flew from the seat of the man's trousers but he continued running. Macklin fired, sending more lint in the air. The man let out a yell, then disappeared in the darkness. Suddenly a very attractive young woman ran out of the house shouting:

"You're shooting the wrong man!" she yelled.

"How the hell do you know who I'm supposed to be shooting?" Jess asked angrily.

"You're looking for Howard Wingate aren't you?"

"Are you trying to tell me that he's not Wingate?"

"That's exactly what I'm telling you! He is not Howard Wingate!!"

"Well, who in the hell is he?"

"That's Jim Lantz."

Jess turned to the deputies and said, "Let's fan out and try to find the poor bastard or he'll bleed to death out there."

They searched the area for about an hour and a half without success. One of the deputies found fresh foot prints on the shoulder of the road, and approximately two miles from the house. Jim Lantz apparently was able to get a ride to town—so the search was called off. Sheriff Macklin had a list of all local doctors in his office, and it was obvious that Mr. Lantz was in great need of one. Within forty-five minutes Lantz was located and brought to Macklins office. He could neither sit or stand up straight as the result of two double-O shotgun blasts.

Sweeten began the questioning. "Jim, you damn near lost your life tonight. I told you who I was. Why did you run?"

"Yes, but I didn't believe that for one damn minute. I thought you was her husband."

"Her husband?"

"Yeah, he said if he caught me with his wife again, he'd kill me. And I thought he was just trying to get close enough to shoot me."

"If the woman is married, why go over there?"

"Sheriff, did you get a good look at her?"

"Yes, she's very pretty."

"Well, now you know."

After Jess and Macklin sent the deputies home, they drove back to Howard Wingate's home. His mother had told a pack of lies that could have been disastrous.

"Howard Wingate!" said Macklin angrily, "was not at the McCormick house, and you knew it. Now, Mrs. Wingate, you almost caused the death of an innocent man tonight, so I want the truth, or by damn you're going to jail!"

Mrs. Wingate began crying softly. After a few minutes she composed herself then invited in. "You just don't know what it is to have a wayward son. I know what he did, but I'm still his mother."

"I sympathize with you Mrs. Wingate, but I have a warrant for his arrest on bank robbery charges, and I intend to serve it," said Jess.

There was a long silence as the woman rocked back and forth in her rocker. Suddenly, she arose from her chair, took a deep breath and said, "If you'll excuse me for a minute, I'll get my coat." It was two o'clock in the morning. *Why did she need a coat.* Jess glanced at Macklin who also was astonished at the woman's actions. A few minutes later, the woman walked from the bedroom fully dressed, and carrying a lantern. "Follow me gentlemen." she said with a troubled voice, "and I'll take you to him."

Macklin and Sweeten followed the woman up a dark trail that led up a steep hill for what seemed like thirty minutes. Then the frail old woman began to whistle. She walked a few more steps and whistled again. Swinging the lantern from side to side. Macklin began to suspect a trap. Jess released the safety on his .45 but kept it holstered. The old woman walked a little farther. They could hear rustling sounds deep in the thick underbrush. She whistled once more, and a figure appeared from the bushes. It was Howard Wingate.

"Howard, turn around and put your hands on your head! "Sweeten said. Macklin placed the cuff's on the robber and Jess quickly frisked him for concealed weapons. He was armed with a .45 automatic pistol and a long blade pocket knife known as a Dallas Special.

They drove Wingate to Macklin's office then transferred him to Jess' car. And one hour later, the last of the robbers had been placed in the Athens jail. Wingate had his portion of the loot in his coat pocket.

At nine o'clock the next morning, Jess took Wingate to the Eustace bank. He was immediately identified as the man who went behind the counter and scooped up the money. He was returned to the Athens jail. Charges of bank robbery were filed against all three suspects.

The preliminary hearings were held the following day, January 14, 1933. Bonds were set at five thousand dollars for Pettit and Williams. Wingate's bond was double that amount. Pettit and Williams made bond. Wingate was unable to make his.

In the February term of the Judicial District Court a grand jury was impaneled by the district judge. Indictments were returned against the three men for armed robbery. Williams and Pettit were re-arrested and bound over for the next term of the district court which was to be in session in April.

Again, Pettit and Williams made bond. Wingate was unable to raise the money. Then, while out on bond, Emmit began drinking heavily. He was on his way home one afternoon and turned his car over, breaking his neck. He died instantly.

Howard Wingate pleaded guilty and was sentenced to fifty years in prison. Lindsey Williams was never brought to trial.

THE DINGLER STILL

"Jess!" said the angry voice on the telephone, "I was fishing out there on the Trinity River about three miles south of Trinidad this morning and Otto Dingler shot a hole in my boat. What you gonna' do about it?"

"Wait a minute," said the sheriff. "How do you know it was Otto Dingler?"

"I saw him!—Him and his big ugly brother. They were out there cooking whiskey!"

"Cooking whiskey!"

"Yeah, right there beside the river."

Otto and Otis Dingler supplied much of the county with bootleg whiskey. Otto was a huge gorilla of man. He weighed about three hundred and fifty pounds and stood six foot six. He had dark brown shoulder-length hair that hung in long matted, uneven strands down his back. He had a long bush-like beard that covered the whole bib of his overalls.

Otto was slightly retarded. His brother, Otis, was smaller and much thinner than his brother. Otis was the brains of the outfit.

Neither had ever been married. Many in that area thought Otto and Otis were allowed to make whiskey because the law was afraid of them. They were overheard telling a big spending customer they'd kill any law-dog that set foot on their property.

The truth was that Jess had busted up over two hundred stills in two years and the previous sheriff had busted up over two hundred and fifty. The Dingler still was well hidden and almost impossible to reach without being spotted long before the law could get there. It was protected by the river on the west side and thick woods and underbrush on the east.

The only way a lawman stood a chance of catching them in the act was to sneak in alone. The place was rumored to have trip-wires and booby traps everywhere. For every still the law busted up during prohibition, ten more would take its place. It was a never ending battle. Not a single lawman supported prohibition. It was a stupid law and served no purpose whatsoever. There were more drunks wandering the streets during those years than at any time in our history. People are going to drink one way or another—legally or illegally.

"Jess you be real careful," said M. G. Jepsen. "We've had Otto in jail before, and it was not a pretty sight. It took Sheriff Baker, five of his deputies and the city marshall to lock that thing up."

"What did he do?"

"He was over at the produce lot and got bit on the arm by a farmer's mule. Not bad. Just broke the skin. Well, Otto pulled a pocket knife and cut the mule's throat. The mule stood right there and bled to death. It was a hell of a mess. The judge said he had to pay the man a hundred dollars for the mule or spend a month in jail. Otto told the judge to go to hell. Thirty days later, we had to let him go. We were afraid to release him while he was awake. So, we waited until he fell asleep, then we opened the door and ran like hell."

Finding the place took several hours of driving back and forth down a wagon-rut road, but Jess finally found a mail box that was hidden in the high weeds near a foot path which led to house. To make sure he had the right address, Jess looked inside to see if they had any mail. If they did, he'd take it to them. But the old mail box was rusty, and the only thing he saw was an empty wasp nest and a few rat droppings.

He parked the car in high weeds then followed the foot path for about a half-mile to an old shack of a house that looked as though a good strong wind would blow it over. It was about halfway between the road and the river.

Usually, a whiskey peddler would leave his dog chained at the house and, if the law showed up, somebody in the house would turn the dog loose. The dog would then run to the still, and when the dog showed up the bootleggers would know the law was out looking for the operation.

Jess saw a gray-eyed, mangy looking Catahoula cur dog in the shade of the porch, but it wasn't chained. It didn't seem to mind a visit from the Henderson County Sheriff because it had a head full of ticks and a back full of fleas. The poor thing had scratched all the hair off its left shoulder. However, it did look toward the sheriff once or twice, so you couldn't say it was a totally useless.

Jess searched through the house and found it to be empty. He smelled the faint odor of sour mash filtering through the thick woods.

The odor grew stronger near the river, so he followed the smell—being very careful to watch for trip-wires.

He carefully made his way through thick underbrush until he located a trip wire near a large fifty-five gallon oil drum that was set back about twenty yards from the cooker which was located in a thick stand of wild persimmon trees. Another trip-wire was spotted between the cooker and the river. Then he noticed Otto washing jars in the river. Otis was spotted near the large cooking vessel, carefully tending a smokeless fire.

Jess knelt in the high underbrush for a good twenty minutes to observe and form a plan. He sure didn't want to go in there and be surprised by a third man hiding in the bushes somewhere. Jess always made it a point to be extra cautious when approaching the unknown.

Apparently, the only weapon the bootleggers had was leaning against a large red-oak near the river bank. The well oiled Winchester was a good distance from both men.

Jess waited a few more minutes to make sure he had the element of surprise, then rose from his crouched position and casually walked to the tree. He kicked the rifle halfway across the water and said, "Good morning, gentlemen. You're under arrest."

Otis ran toward him with a hot fire-poker and Jess dropped him with a straight right that knocked him out cold. The only thing Jess had underestimated was the speed of big Otto Dingler. The big gorilla was on him before he knew what happened. Otto had both the sheriff's arms pinned to his sides in a lung bursting bear-hug.

Jess was unable to pull either pistol. The strength of Otto was squeezing the life out of him. The only thing Jess could do was to try and trip him. It was his one chance to jar the man's arms loose.

Jess managed to get one leg between Otto's and shift the big man's balance. Then by jerking his body, he was able to make the man fall backward. The fall did not free Otto's arms from Jess' waist. Breathing was extremely difficult with Otto's weight pressing on his ribs.

Suddenly, Jess found himself being pulled toward the water. If Otto was able to drag Jess out in that water, especially with the strength the man had, he knew he'd be a goner for sure. Clearly, Otto Dingler was the strongest man he had ever run up against.

What if Otis wakes up? *He'd help his brother drown me!* Jess' mind raced. He knew he had to do something and do it pretty quick. He couldn't move his arms in any direction, up, down or sideways. But maybe he could lock one leg around a stump near the water. If he could, Otto would have to use one hand to pry it away.

It worked! Otto used his left hand to pull Jess' leg away from the stump—which was a terrible mistake. Jess took aim at Otto's chin—knocking him backward. He quickly jumped to his feet and swung a hard right to Otto's nose, which sent him sliding down the muddy river bank and in the water. The game was over. All Otto could do when he came up was look down the barrel of a forty-five. Jess glanced toward Otis to make sure he was still out. He was. Now, the only thing Otto could do was holler.

"Come out here and fight like a man!"

Otto's strength had surprised Jess, and he was not about to go out in the water. That would give brother Otis time to wake up and find another piece of artillery.

Otto began to splash the water toward Jess. "Come on! fight like a man you damn coward!!"

Jess took aim at Otto's leg. "No, but I tell you what I will do. If you don't come out of there I'll shoot you in the leg."

Otto continued a barrage of cussing, spitting and waving his arms in a vein attempt to invite Jess to a battle.

"I'll count to three, damn you!"

"That gun don't skeer' me none!"

"One!"

"Jess, you ain't a fart in a whirlwind!"

"Two"

"Coward!"

"Three!"

"Go ahead n' shoot! I don't give a shit!"

Jess fired. The thunderous sound echoed as the bullet pierced Otto's right leg two inches above his knee. Otto just stood there and watched the blood run down his leg and turn the water red. Otto had a funny-looking grin on his face as the blood oozed from his overalls.

"Hell, that didn't hurt."

"Well, it's going to hurt if you don't come on out of there," Jess answered.

"Well, what are you gonna' do if I don't come out?"

"Then I'll shoot you in the other leg."

Otto wouldn't budge so Jess took aim at the other leg. Otto stretched out his right hand and said, "Wait! Wait a minute! I think it's starting to hurt...just wait one more minute! If it starts hurting real bad then I'll come out."

Jess waited thirty seconds.

"Oh!...damn! It hurts! Alright, I'm coming out!"

Otis tied a tourniquet around his brother's leg when he woke up. Together they hobbled up the foot path, stopping just long enough for Otis to throw a couple of rocks at his guard dog.

Jess and Jepsen returned later that afternoon and destroyed the still. Otis was sent to jail for a month and paid a fine of three hundred dollars. Otto was sent to the Terrell Mental Hospital, where he was pronounced unstable.

Three months later Otto escaped from the mental hospital and was never heard from again.

Old Rangers Never Die

THE PATTON CASE

The Patton Home

A woman named Florence Everett drove from her home in Tennessee Colony to Sand Flat community to pick up her daughter, Carrie, her husband, Johnny McGehee, and the two children. Carrie had promised to have Thanksgiving dinner with Florence if she would pick them up. They did not own a car.

For the past few months, the McGehee's had been living in the same two-room house with a fifty-two-year-old farmer named George Patton. The two men had planned to sharecrop Patton's fifty-four acre farm.

Florence arrived at the Patton place around eight-thirty in the morning. She was in a hurry because she had a turkey in the oven. However, when she knocked on the door of Patton's two-room shack, George told her that Johnny and Carrie had left the night before. He said that two of Johnny's friends had found him a job in the oil fields somewhere around Seminole, Oklahoma.

Florence was very upset. She told the farmer that Carrie would never leave without first telling her. She called the farmer a liar, then drove straight to the Henderson County sheriff.

Florence learned that Sheriff Joel Baker had been defeated by a 24-year-old ex deputy named Jess Sweeten, but he promised to talk to the farmer about her missing family.

Baker questioned Patton for several hours but found no holes in his story. Everything the farmer told him seemed reasonable. It was the depression years, and many families over the past year had suddenly packed up and moved to greener pastures. Work was scarce during the depression; sixty-five thousand workers a day were loosing their jobs in the United States alone.

"It takes time to get settled in," said the sheriff," and since I've lost the election, you'll be dealing with the new sheriff anyway."

Florence waited for three months and still no word from her family.

She asked Johnny's family if they had received any news .They had not. She returned to the Patton farm and confronted the farmer a second time.

"Mrs. Everett, they moved off in the middle of the night," the farmer repeated.

"Then why have I not heard from them?" she demanded.

"Well, I can't tell what I don't know."

Florence returned home and wrote letters to the newspaper in Seminole, Oklahoma. She wrote letters to relatives of Johnny McGehee who lived in other states. There was still no word. She spent her and husband Harold's life savings trying to find the family.

Jess Sweeten was now the new sheriff of Henderson County. Florence knew nothing about the "Boy Sheriff" except what she had read in the local papers. Articles in various papers reported that he was a tall, good looking man, and very popular. From what she had read, Jess Sweeten seemed to be more celebrity than sheriff.

Knocking on the door-frame of his office, she understood what the girls saw in the man. He was as handsome as a movie star and a great deal of charm, but he seemed much to young to be a sheriff. How could a man of that young age find a missing family without years of experience to guide him? Oh my Lord, she thought to herself as she took a seat next to Sweeten's roll-top desk.

Jess was signing a small stack of court papers while Deputy Sheriff Homer Williams waited with a shackled prisoner named Lon Overstreet. Jess placed the papers inside a large envelope, sealed it shut, then ordered Homer to remove the prisoner's handcuffs. Jess placed the package in Lon Overstreet's hand and said, "Give this to Warden Waid when you get to Huntsville. And tell him to call me as soon as you get down there."

Homer Williams had a surprised look on his face.

"Jess, I can run him down there."

"No, Homer. I need you to go to Brownsboro. He knows the way. Lon, you've got three days!"

Homer became worried.

"Jess, suppose he heads for the high country?"

"Then I'll track him down and kill him!"

Lon sheepishly nodded his head with a grin and said," Sheriff, I'll be there in three days. You can count on me. But, can I stop by the house an visit with my folks before I go?"

Jess nodded his approval, waved his hand as though shooing a fly, then focused his attention on Florence Everett.

Homer led Lon to the front door, ordering him to follow the sheriff's instructions to the letter. He pointed toward the Highway Nineteen road marker and said, "You take that highway and keep going until you get there."

He followed Lon for about a block, continuously warning the young man of his peril should he fail to arrive within three days' time.

Florence gripped her purse tightly while waiting for Jess to finish the paperwork.

"Yes, ma'am," he said, "What can I do for you?"

"Sheriff, my name is Florence Everett. I want to report my family missing. They've been missing since the day before Thanksgiving, last November."

Jess took a clean sheet of paper from the bottom drawer of his desk and wrote her name on the top, right-hand corner.

"Where did they come up missing from? Where did they live?"

"With George Patton."

"Where does George live?"

"Eight miles north of Athens, in Sand Flat community."

"Do you know the name of the road?"

"No. I don't think it has a name. It's the one that goes past the graveyard. You turn left at that road, then take another left at the top of the hill near a place they call Chinquipin Ridge."

"What are the names?"

"Carrie, that's my daughter's name. And her husband is J. W. McGehee. Also my two grand babies, Bobby and Doyle."

"Why were they living with George?"

"They were supposed to sharecrop some corn this year."

Jess continued writing the information as Florence searched her purse for a handkerchief. Failing to find one, she wiped her eyes with her hand then continued before Jess was finished taking notes.

"Sheriff, I'm at my wits' end. I just don't know what else to do. I've wrote letters to newspapers. I've placed ads all over the place. I've talked to Sheriff Baker—"

Jess interrupted. "I assume you've talked to George. What did he say?"

"Sheriff, George Patton is a liar. He said they moved up to Oklahoma. He said J. W. got a job up in the oil fields. J.W. don't know a single thing about that kind of work. And Carrie would never leave without telling me first, not in a million years."

"Do you have photographs of the family?"

"They're just snap-shots."

"I'll go talk to George, but in the meantime, see if you can locate those photographs. Where do you live?"

"I live in Tennessee Colony."

Jess wrote her address near the bottom of the paper then placed it in the top drawer with a great number of other papers. After closing the drawer, Florence became extremely anxious. To her, it was as though Jess had simply filed it away. And she was not leaving his office without knowing he'd help find her family.

"Sheriff," she pleaded, "I know how busy you are. And sometimes a thing like this has a way getting pushed to the back burner.

But I want you to promise me that you'll find my family, no matter what. You're my only hope, so please promise."

Jess removed the paper from the desk and placed it in his shirt pocket.

"Mrs. Everett," he said solemnly. "If your family can be found, I'll find them."

"Sheriff, can I count on your word?"

"I'll find them, Mrs. Everett. One way or another. You have my word."

Placing his hand on Florence's shoulder in an effort to reassure the promise, he walked her to the door. After she left he immediately drove to the Patton farm. It took the better part of an hour to locate the place, because that part of the county had a lot of dirt roads that ended at some farmer's pasture.

Finally, he located the place by asking a neighbor named Hawley. Mr. Hawley lived at the end of the cemetery road. After explaining that he and his family had voted for Jess Sweeten in the last election, the man pointed him toward Patton's place with a warning about the deep sand.

"That road to Patton's place!" warned Mr. Hawley, "has sand so deep it will bog a car all the way to the axle."

George Patton was a life-long bachelor. He was fifty-two years old. He wore a black Stetson hat and cowboy boots, and for the past twelve years had worked at the Royal and Henry Feed Company in Athens.

He was well respected but pitifully poor. In his younger years he had been a cowboy who worked the Wild West shows from Cheyenne, Wyoming to Canada. He was an accomplished fiddle player but had never won the fiddling contest held in Athens each year.

Patton was in the field plowing when he noticed a trail of dust coming up the road. He stopped his mule, then walked to the front yard and greeted the Sheriff with a huge smile.

"Howdy, Sheriff," he said, as Jess stopped in the front yard. "You know, when folks come down this road, they're either lost or they want to see me. And you don't look lost. So what can I do for you?"

Jess stepped out of the car and shook hands with the farmer. "No George I'm not lost, I'm looking for the McGehee family. I'm told they lived out here with you."

George removed his hat, wiped sweat from the inside brim, then led Jess to a shade tree near the barn.

"Yeah, they did. They lived here for about three months."

"Do you know where they are?"

"Not exactly. It's like I told Mrs. Everett. One night around midnight, these two fellers drove out here. They pulled into the yard, about where your car is now, and honked the horn. J. W. got out of bed and walked outside to talk to them. He must have talked for about five or ten minutes then of a sudden, he come running back in the house all excited, and said to Carrie.' Honey, get up and get your duds on, we're going to the oil fields'."

"Did those men ever get out of the car?"

"No, they stayed in the car and kept gunning the motor like they was in a big hurry."

"What type of job did he have up there?"

"Roughneck I guess."

"Were you upset about J. W. leaving like that?"

"Yeah, it upset me pretty good. I got out of bed and put my britches on. I said to Johnny, 'this throws a monkey wrench in my plans. I thought we were going to grow a big crop of corn and split it down the middle. I had done went and quit my job at the feed store.'"

"What did Carrie say?"

"Carrie sez to me, George, we love you like a daddy, but we can make five dollars a day up there, and we can't do that in this country! So I sez to Johnny, 'why don't you tell them fellers to get out? Let's build a pot of coffee and talk it over.' But he sez 'George, we don't have no time. We got to get on up there and be ready for work.'"

"This oil field. Was it close to a town?"

"Yes, sir. Seminole, Oklahoma."

Jess tapped his boot against the tree to knock several large ants from the toe. His eyes roamed the fifty-four acre farm. The house was a small-two room shack with thin board-and-bat siding and a tin roof.

"George, can you think of a reason why Carrie wouldn't write her mother and let her know where they were?"

"Well, that part don't bother me none, Sheriff. Knowing them wildcatters, they're more than likely stuck way out on some oil lease in the middle of nowhere; no car or nothing. It's the rainy season up there."

"Well, George, I appreciate your time."

Jess drove to the home of Florence Everett in Tennessee Colony. He collected the photographs. Later he had them enlarged at the Ned Chalmers Studio, then mailed the pictures to the sheriff in Seminole, Oklahoma along with a letter asking that he post the photographs in all public buildings. He also requested that the sheriff send a deputy out to each wildcatter in the area.

While waiting on a reply from Seminole, Jess visited the Patton farm no less than ten times. Each visit began with talk of peas, politics or corn, but it always ended with a question about the missing McGehee family.

He noticed the more he visited Patton, the more annoyed the farmer became, so he planned the visits at specific times. Each visit was designed to interfere with Patton's daily routine. One visit would be planned at daybreak. That was the time George fed his stock. Another visit came at hoeing time when, more often than not, George was working in the field.

Another visit would come in the late afternoon when he was feeding chickens, repairing harness and equipment. But when Jess brought the word from Oklahoma, George was eating lunch.

Jess didn't wait for the farmer to come to the door, he just knocked on the door frame then walked directly to the kitchen table and sat down opposite the surprised farmer who had a mouth full of beans. Jess pulled a letter from his coat pocket and laid it on the table.

"George, I wrote a letter to the sheriff up in Seminole, Oklahoma. He posted photographs of the McGehee family in every public building in the county. His deputies paid a visit to all the wildcat wells. Nobody up there recognized them or had ever heard of a family named McGehee."

George continued eating without showing the least bit of concern. He folded a slice of bread, dipped it in the bean juice, then shoved the entire wad in his mouth.

"Well, that's where they said they were going."

"George, there must be another reason why Carrie won't write her mother. It's got me stumped. But you and I both know that Carrie's had plenty of time to write a letter. Can you think of a reason why she won't write a damn letter?"

George sopped the last of his pinto bean juice with a fresh slice of bread and said, "Well, Sheriff, I didn't tell you this before, because I didn't think it was any of my business. But, Carrie had a step daddy.

She hated him. And J. W. had a step momma. They couldn't get along for ten minutes. If I was looking for a reason...that would be it."

"I was not aware of that, George, but you could be right. I appreciate your help."

Jess shook the farmer's hand, then walked to his car and drove away.

The first thing a lawman looks for in a criminal investigation is the unusual. And so far the only unusual thing in this case was the fact that Carrie had not written to her mother. All families will fight at one time or another. That's normal. But, in most cases they will always let some family member know where they were. They may fight like cats and dogs but they still love each other.

Jess drove to Tennessee Colony.

"Mrs. Everett, does Carrie have a step daddy?"

"Yes."

"Does she love him?"

"Well, of course she does! Harold adopted her when she was six months old. She's never known another daddy."

He talked to the neighbors of Florence Everett, and all said the same thing. Carrie loved her step daddy. He talked to Johnny's parents and neighbors. One thing was clear. Both Carrie and J. W. loved their step-parents, and George Patton had told a lie.

On the way back to Athens Jess recalled Patton saying that Carrie HAD a step daddy. And when talking about Johnny's stepmother, he used the same word HAD. If Carrie and J. W. were alive, they'd still HAVE step-parents.

He returned to the Patton farm.

"George, that story about Carrie not liking her step daddy won't hold water. I talked to her mother. I talked to all her friends and neighbors. They all told me that Carrie loved her step daddy. Harold adopted her when she was only six months old. I talked to J. W's folks and all their neighbors. They all say the same thing."

"Well, I can't help that, Sheriff. All I know is what she told me at the supper table. She said she wished I was her daddy. Maybe Harold done something to her a long time ago and she never told her momma about it. Things like that happen all the time."

"Well, George, again I thank you for your time."

Without asking more questions, Jess suddenly turned on his heel and walked toward the car. George paused in the doorway until Jess closed the car door, then he walked over and propped his foot on the running board.

"Sheriff," said the farmer seriously, "I've told you everything I know about it. I wish I could help you more but I can't. And I sure hate to see you waste time and gasoline driving all the way out here."

Jess started the car, flipped a cigarette butt out the window and said, "Oh, I'll be back from time to time, George. You can count on that—until I find them. And I think I will.

The next morning, Jess drove to The Royall and Henry Feed store and talked to the owner.

"Mr. Royall, did you have an employee by the name of George Patton?"

"Yes I did, Sheriff. And I wish I still had him. Why?"

"Well, there was a family living with him out there, and they've come up missing."

"Surely you don't suspect that George Patton had anything to do with their disappearance, do you, Sheriff?"

"Well, I don't know yet. I'd like to know a little more about him. I was hoping that you could tell me."

"Well, one thing is for certain. If you think George had anything to do with the disappearance of that family, you'd be wrong. George is not that kind of man. You could talk to anybody in this county and they'd tell you the same thing. He's the most honest man I've ever known, bar none! He worked here for twelve years. He refused to take paid vacations or paid holidays to save money to buy that old sticker burr farm. We tried our best to talk him out of it, but his mind was set. So I told him that Roosevelt was starting a new program for the farmer. Sheriff, George refused to take free money. He felt, and rightly so, that a man ought to work for what he gets. If he don't, he'll grow lazy and become dependent."

"Is George a truthful man?"

"Well, I've never caught him in a lie. Jess, Will Justice was raised with George. They went to school together. Why don't you go over there and talk to him?"

"Thanks, Mr. Royall, I'll do that."

Jess drove to the law offices of Justice and Sigler. Richard Sigler, Will's partner, hated Jess Sweeten with a passion. Jess had confiscated his slot machines when he first took office, and the case was still in litigation. Jess claimed that the machines were illegal gaming devices, while Richard claimed that they were used for entertainment purposed only. He was not happy to see Jess Sweeten.

Will Justice, on the other hand, could care less one way or the other. He was a well respected attorney in Henderson County. Richard loved money. Will Justice loved the law. Will was the only one to acknowledge the new sheriff.

"Good morning, Jess. What can I do for you?"

"Morning, Will, do you know a fellow by the name of George Patton?"

"Yes, I do. I went to school with him over in the free state of Van Zandt. Why?"

"Then you know him pretty well?"

"Yes, you could say that."

"What could you tell me about him?"

"In what way?"

"Oh, what type of man he is. That sort of thing."

"Well, the first word that comes to mind is poor. He's as poor as a church mouse. The second is honesty. So, I'd say he's just a poor ol' honest farmer."

"Do you think he's capable of violence?"

"Oh, good lord no! Jess, that man is totally incapable of violence. You're not seriously suspecting him of such a thing are you?"

"Well, a family that lived with him for several months disappeared."

Richard angrily interrupted the conversation.

"Will! He's talking about those McGehee's! Sheriff Baker investigated that disappearance a long time ago. That family moved off to California like a million other people for Christ's sake! Those people are just looking for work."

Jess turned and walked out the door. Richard hollered as the door closed: "You take good care of those machines of mine Sheriff. I'll be over to pick them up pretty soon!"

Jess could hear Richard's voice through the door so he mumbled his answer.

"Yeah, you can pick them up, Richard. When hell turns to icicles."

This case was like an itch that Jess couldn't scratch. If there was a body he would have something to go on. A gut feeling told him that the solution to the case would be found somewhere on the Patton farm. It was time for another visit to Mr. Honest Farmer.

"George, I need to look around. I hope you don't mind."

"Sheriff, I done told you everything I know."

Jess walked to the barn, looked at all the equipment, opened boxes, searched the feed room. He searched the chicken pen and corn crib. He shined a light under the house. He searched the smoke house and got stung by a yellow-jacket. He was about ready to give up when he noticed a plank nailed at an odd angle on the side of the house.

A closer examination of the board revealed no less than twenty nails had secured the plank to the outer wall. Each nail was spaced about a half inch apart. For some reason George wanted to make sure the board stayed put.

"George, what's this board doing up here?"

"I covered a hole with it."

Jess stared at the board for several moments then walked toward the front door. As they walked George trailed close behind answering more questions.

"George, what kind of woman was Carrie McGehee?"

"What do you mean Sheriff?"

"Oh, sometimes when folks live this close together, especially with a woman—a young, pretty woman..."

George became visibly irritated. He interrupted the question as Jess stepped inside the door.

"Sheriff, let me tell you something! Carrie was a decent woman! She was about the finest woman you've ever met. That woman never said a cuss word in her life; never used slang words at all. For you to suggest that she was that kind of woman, you're wrong! She was the sweetest, kindest, most decent woman I've ever met. She wasn't like most women. Most women are running all over the country hunting news. She would never dream of doing anything like that!"

Jess continued walking to the bedroom opposite the hole on the outer wall. George cut a wad of from a plug of tobacco to calm his nerves. He chewed for several moments, then spat a stream of tobacco in a porcelain bed-pot.

Jess noticed a two-foot square piece of cardboard had been tacked to the wall opposite the plank on the outer wall. Again, the farmer had used a great number of tacks.

Jess cut a portion from the center of the cardboard and exposed a hole made by a shotgun blast. A good number of the pellets were still embedded in the wall. Several appeared to be coated with a rust colored substance. Jess pried several pellets loose then placed them in an envelope.

"What happened here, George?"

"I shot a cat."

"This is at least four-and-a-half foot up. How in the world did that cat get up this high?"

"It come in here one night about midnight and knocked a bottle over. The noise woke me up, so I grabbed my shot gun. I must have scared it when I went for the gun because it jumped up. And when it did, I blasted him."

Jess pried several more pellets from the wall. Each pellet had the rust colored substance on the shot.

"How did you see it?"

"What do you mean?"

Jess placed the envelope in his coat pocket.

"It was midnight!...How did you see it?"

"I struck a match!"

"You lit a match. Damn, George. If you lit a match at that time of night...all you'd see is the flame."

"I can't help it, Sheriff. That's how it happened."

"Show me, George. Just lay down on the bed over there and pretend the cat just walked in. Do everything exactly the way you did that night so I can get it clear in my mind."

George reluctantly complied and his attempt was comical. He reached under the bed with his right hand, lit the match with his left, then held it beside the barrel of the weaving shotgun and pretended to shoot. The whole process took about fifteen seconds to complete.

"George, that cat would be half way to Van Zandt County before you could squeeze the trigger."

He ran his hand over the hole, then extended it, palm outward, toward Patton.

"Where is the hair?

"What hair?"

The Patton Case

"George, if you shot a cat, the hair would be imbedded in the wall. There ain't a single hair on this wall!"

"I can't help that, Sheriff. That's what happened."

That afternoon, Jess took the pellets to the Landon C. Moore Laboratory in Dallas, Texas. Three hours later, he learned that the rust colored material on the shot was human blood. Not animal, as the farmer had said.

He phoned Homer Williams and told him to round up as many volunteers as he could. They were to meet him at the Patton farm no later than eight o'clock the next morning. They were to bring probes and shovels.

"Tell them to be prepared to stay all day, so bring food."

At dawn, cars, trucks and wagons lined the narrow road to the Patton farm. Homer had rounded up a crowd of over two hundred people. They were all waiting in the farmer's front yard. Patton was not home at the time; he was helping Mr. Hawley cut firewood, so he was totally unaware of Jess' plan for several hours.

Jess stepped to the front of the crowd and said, "Ladies and gentlemen, I want to thank you all for coming out here this morning. I suspect George Patton of murder, and we're here to dig for the bodies. I don't know if we'll find anything or not but we're going to try. I want the men with the probes to go first. Fan out in a long line—starting in front   yard, and probe the ground. If you find a soft spot, mark it with a flag and the men with shovels will dig. Remember one thing. I only suspect George so you treat his home with respect. We'll fill all the holes before we leave."

The Patton Farm Yard

Within two hours the Patton farm resembled a battlefield. No less than fifteen holes appeared in the front yard and approximately twenty or so in the back. Homer Williams led a number of the men on a spot-search throughout the fifty-four acre farm, including a wooded portion to the south.

The women rolled two fifty-five gallon oil drums to the shade of large tree. They placed several wide planks over the barrels for a makeshift table. Apparently, the barrels had used for rendering lard because each barrel was coated with a greasy rancid smelling substance. A red-checkered table cloth was spread over the planks to help conceal the foul odor.

George returned home at ten thirty in the morning demanding the names and addresses of all the volunteers. He was extremely upset that The a number of his acquaintances and friends were digging up his farm. Jess met him near the gate and said, "George, I had the pellets analyzed up in Dallas. The rust colored material on those pellets proved to be human blood. You told me that you shot a house cat. Now you could save us a lot of trouble by telling me where you buried the bodies."

"Sheriff, I've told you the truth."

At noon, the digging was half way across the back pasture. Several volunteers climbed the back fence toward the woods in an effort to save time, knowing that dirt will sometimes settle lower if the graves are shallow, and the grass will be green if the soil has been turned.

Two men found a rather large bone in the back pasture. They ran to Jess and excitedly presented the evidence to the young sheriff. Jess gave it a quick glance then threw it to the side. It was obviously the leg bone of a cow.

The yard contained many small bone fragments, but they were broken into small pieces and appeared to be table-scraps. Frank Slayton, a friend of Patton, began probing around the house but stopped when he noticed George sitting on a rawhide chair near the back steps. George looked pitiful. His face was ashen white, and he had a blank stare on his face. Frank felt deep sympathy toward his friend. He leaned the probe against the house then eased toward Patton.

"George, we're just supporting our sheriff. You got to respect that."

George refused to look his friend in the eye, instead, he continued watching the diggers. He answered in the voice of a victim, low and barely audible.

"Frank, how long have you known me?"

Frank leaned against the house, his voice almost matching that of Patton's.

"About twenty years, George."

"Frank, did I ever take food out of your mouth?"

"No."

George took a deep breath. There was a long pause as he filled a pipe with tobacco.

"Have I ever hurt you or your family in any way?"

Frank grew slightly nervous, but answered seriously, "No, George, you never did."

George packed the tobacco with his thumb.

"Ever knowed me to steal, Frank?"

Again Frank answered in a low tone. "George, you're the most honest man I've ever known in my whole life."

With that, the farmer turned his misty blue eyes toward Frank for the first time. His voice cracking with emotion. "Well, the Sheriff thinks I killed four people—two babies! Do you believe I could do something like that?"

Frank looked toward the ground as though he was ashamed of himself. He had suddenly realized the seriousness of the matter. "George, I don't know what to say."

George rubbed his chin whiskers, then looked off in the distance. He remained silent for a long time before lighting a match. His eyes focused on the tree line at the back pasture. "I don't know what to say either, Frank."

The silence was broken by the shrill voice of a woman. "Come and get it!"

The woman was banging two pieces of pipe together. A fifty-pound block of ice was chopped in a large washtub while the dirty and exhausted men lined up to be served. Plates were piled high with chicken, ham and pot roast. Every imaginable vegetable was being served, from black-eye peas to pinto beans.

"It's just like graveyard work." remarked one of the women.

"Honey, it is graveyard working." said another.

When all the men were served, one of the ladies noticed George sitting by himself. She asked Jess if it was alright to invite him over. Jess nodded his approval.

She quickly walked to the pitiful looking farmer and said, "George, it's time to eat. Come on over and get a plate." He answered in a sheepish whisper. "Mrs. Davis, I don't think I should."

She grabbed him by his shirt sleeve and pulled him toward the table. "Nonsense George, we've got enough food here to feed an army. Now, get your bony behind over there or them chickens are going to think you was foolish!"

Suddenly a smile came on the farmers face. "Are you sure they won't mind?"

"George, they have no choice in the matter. Now get on over there and get them groceries!"

Several women heaped his plate with so much food it ran off the edge. One woman proudly placed several larger rutabagas on top of large, thick ham slices. George made sure her back was turned before accidentally spilling them on the ground.

Frank and a few other men made room under a tree, and soon were laughing and telling jokes. Frank asked why the sheriff suspected him of such a thing in the first place.

"Publicity! Frank. Just look around. He's got two hundred voters out here thinking he's doing something real important for the county and come voting time, all these folks are going to remember his little picnic. It's called politics. This is how Jess Sweeten got elected in the first place. He knows how to deal with those newspaper boys. Heck, they need stories to sell them papers with. And boy does he give them the stories. "

Frank looked at Melvin.

"Well, I'll be dammed."

George shook his head. "No, Frank...I'll be dammed. You see, it ain't important for him to find anything. Most of these folks are going to think I'm guilty because he said so. He can just prance all over the county saying...'Oh! he's guilty!' I just couldn't prove it."

Melvin glanced hatefully toward Jess Sweeten. "George, you need a lawyer."

George pointed toward the shack of a house. "Does it look like I can afford a lawyer? hell I'm pore-folks. I could sell everything I got and it would pay for maybe one round."

Frank thought for a moment then asked, "What about Will Justice? You know him."

George chuckled, "I've known Will Justice all my life. I couldn't buy the hay for one of his nightmares."

Melvin had a suggestion. "What about Richard Siglar? He hates Jess. I'll bet he'd take the case out of spite. "What did Jess do to him?"

"Well, Richard bought a bunch of slot machines and put'em all over the county; and he was making a pretty good living too. But then Jess went out there and picked 'em up. He said it was agin' the law. Richard lost a fortune. Man, he was mad enough to kick a hog bare-footed."

Jess kept an eye on George and his friends. He noticed that Frank, Melvin, and quite a few others called it quits after the meal. But two thirds remained. When they finished eating, they entered the back pasture through the wooden gate. When the last man entered the pasture, he closed it behind him. The bottom board on the wooden gate dragged the ground.

Jess marked an X in the sand with the toe of his boot, and ordered two men to dig directly between the gate posts. His eyes remained fixed on the farmer figuring that, if George became nervous or tried to divert his attention, he'd know he was getting warm. But if the digging bothered George Patton, he did not show it.

They dug to a depth of six feet and found no sign of the missing family. The hole was filled, as the sun dropped below the tree line. It had been a long and tiring day. He was thanking those that remained when two men came running from the woods.

"Jess!" Hollered the man. "We found something!"

Jess rushed to meet the two out-of-breath men halfway across the corn field! The man was holding a flower-print shirt. The left side of the shirt appeared to be stained with dried blood. A huge, gaping hole, obviously made by the blast of a shotgun was plainly visible about one inch below the left-hand pocket.

"Where did you find it?" Jess asked.

"In the back pasture! It was under a huge pile of brush."

Jess carefully examined the shirt inside and out. Both pockets were empty. Whoever had been wearing the shirt was no doubt dead as a door-knob because the entire front portion was covered with blood stains. The majority of the shot apparently went through the victim's heart. The unusual thing about the shirt was the print on the fabric. *Why would a man wear a shirt with large blue flowers?* Jess thought to himself. He showed the shirt to Patton.

"What happened here, George?"

"I don't know. I never seen it before."

"I think you did, George. You killed J. W., then took the evidence back there and hid it in a pile of brush. You intended to burn the brush, but changed your mind, thinking that the fire would get out of hand and set the woods on fire. Then as time went by, you forgot all about it."

"J. W. didn't own a shirt like that, Sheriff. Besides lots of hunters go back there. That shirt could belong to anybody.

When Jess presented the shirt to Florence Everett, her eyes immediately filled with tears. She dropped down on the sofa as though all her strength had been sapped. She wept openly for several minutes before Jess asked her to identify the shirt. Clutching it tightly in her hand she said, "I made it from a flour sack."

"Are you sure, Mrs. Everett?"

She held the collar open. "See, this shirt does not have a label. Johnny had three shirts to his name, and two pair of pants. I made this shirt."

Jess sat silently on the sofa as Florence tried in vain to compose herself.

"Sheriff they were all I had. They deserve a Christian funeral...with words. Not in some ditch like a pile of garbage. They were my babies." Her voice strained with the anguish of a mother's love as she held the shirt to her face. Caressing the object as thought it was Johnny himself.

Jess carefully retrieved the shirt then returned it to the large paper sack. "Mrs. Everett, we don't know if they're dead or not. I'll admit it seems likely. But we won't know until we locate the bodies. So lets pray they're still alive some place."

She wiped her eyes with her apron, then cleared her throat. "Sheriff," she said softly, "I know they're dead. I've known it for a long time. A mother who loves her family knows these things. I can't explain it. I didn't want to accept it. But I have now. I just want them to have a decent funeral...and tell them that I love them. I'm a poor woman Sheriff, but poor women love just as deeply as rich women. And I would give everything that I own in this world, including my clothes, to see that it's done."

Jess now understood why a man would wear such an ugly shirt. Johnny was wearing it to show Florence Everett that he appreciated her gift. He knew she was coming to pick them up Thanksgiving Day.

Jess returned to the Patton farm with a renewed determination. He told George that Florence had identified her son-in-law's shirt.

George swore that J. W. would never wear a flower print shirt. "Sheriff," he said, "Mrs. Everett is one of the finest women in the world. I respect her, but she's wrong about that shirt."

Jess knew the old farmer was lying but he knew he would never prove anything until the bodies were found. George Patton would be a tough nut to crack, but he had plenty of time. Like his father always said. "A trail is never cold."

Will Justice met Richard and his mother at the cafe. Harold, the retarded brother of Richard sat in a booth talking to himself and drinking soup from a bowl. Will pulled up a chair and asked Richard if he heard about the fiasco at the Patton farm.

Richard said, "Yes, Melvin Williams told me all about it. Jess is after publicity. Joel Baker said that George was telling the truth and that's good enough for me. He said Jess was just stirring fresh piss in old cow shit, trying to raise a stink."

"Richard, have you talked to George? You know he might need a friend about now."

Mrs. Siglar interrupted. "Both of you ought to do something or Jess Sweeten will just keep on persecuting that poor man. If you allow him to get George in that jail house, he'll beat him to death."

When Harold heard Jess' name, he stood up waving a table knife. "Just cut his damn heart out. If you cut his heart out you can kick it out in the street and let the cars run over it!"

Richard Sigler and his mother often discussed Jess Sweeten in front of Harold, which was a mistake. To Harold, Jess Sweeten was the devil himself. His mental state was getting worse by the day.

Will continued, "I've known George all my life and if there's one man that's incapable of murder it's George Patton."

Mrs. Siglar interrupted again. "I understand that half those people left when they found out he was on a fishing trip."

"Well, Mother, if he's fishing, he forgot to bring a stringer. I'll go talk to George and see if we can help him."

At daybreak, George had just started the fire for his morning coffee when he noticed the familiar trail of dust coming up the road. He did not greet Jess in the usual manner. Instead he poured two cups of coffee and placed one on the opposite side of the table. Jess walked in without knocking and sat down. He sipped the coffee while George fried a pan of bacon and eggs. Then, as George began eating, Jess poured himself another cup of coffee and walked to the bedroom, studying each item. The family pictures atop the four drawer chest. The family bible resting on the dresser. The cotton mattress showing stains where the children had slept. And at the end of the bed stood a large trunk covered with an embroidered doily.

Jess opened the trunk and began tossing its contents on the bed. The trunk was filled with female clothes. Why would George, a life long bachelor keep women's clothing in the house?

When George heard the trunk slide on the floor, he quickly explained from the kitchen. "Now before you start asking a bunch of questions, that trunk belongs to my lady friend."

"What's her name?"

George peered around the door frame. "Nellie Phillips."

Jess continued piling the clothes on the bed. "What are you doing with her clothes George?"

"She didn't want to wag 'em all over the place, so she left 'em here."

Jess held up one of the many dresses. It was the style worn by a young woman. "She visits that often. Does she?"

"From time to time."

"How old is Nellie Phillips?"

George became annoyed at the way Jess was piling the clothes on the bed. He began straightening each parcel." eighteen. Why?"

"Where does she live?"

"She lives in Oklahoma. I pick her up at the depot. She stays down here for a few days and then she goes back home."

"She comes down here naked, does she?"

George was becoming more annoyed. "What are you getting at?"

"All of her clothes are here George. Underwear, lipstick, rouge. Women don't walk off and leave this kind of stuff!"

"Sheriff, you pile clothes just like a kid does when he brings 'em in from the clothes line. You just pile 'em any which away. I got a right to respect someone else's things."

"George, help me take the trunk to the car. You and I are going for a little ride."

"Where are we going?"

Jess placed the trunk in the back seat of the cruiser.

"We're going to Athens."

Jess placed George in a cell on the second floor, then drove to Florence Everett's house in Tennessee Colony. He asked if she could identify the clothing in the trunk. Mrs. Everett said that she could not.

Jess returned to Athens. He questioned George at his office for the remainder of the morning. Within two hours Richard Siglar stormed in unannounced.

"Sheriff, do you intend to file charges against my client, or do I have to get a *habeas corpus*?"

Jess knew that if he said yes, a charge would have to be filed then a hearing by the grand jury with no *corpus delicti*. The grand jury would not indict without the bodies being located.

"No, Richard, he's not under arrest. Not at this time."

Richard drove Patton back home. Jess walked to the depot and asked Paten Bradley, the Negro porter if he knew George Patton. Bradley rubbed his chin and said, "Yes, suh I knows the man. He drives a hack with an ol' plug hoss."

"Did he pick up a lady at the depot?"

Bradley tapped his chin with his fingers then looked toward the sky, "Yes, suh. I'z about to say that! A young lady. I remembers, cause she awful young to be courtin' Mr. George."

"When did he pick her up last?"

"Oh, let's see now. It was a Saturday, 'cuz dat's when it always is. Nearly 'bout two months ago."

"Two months?"

"Yes, suh! Two months."

"Think now! When did he bring her back?"

"He didn't brung her back."

Jess' right eyebrow arched high.

"You know that for certain?"

"Well, suh. If he brung 'er back I wasn't here. And I wuz here all the time; 'cept on Sunday. But they ain't no train on Sunday. Jist a freight train."

If Bradley was right; five people were now unaccounted for. Would there be more? And if so, how many? And where were the bodies?

The barber provided another name. Since there was now a history of missing people connected with George Patton, he felt free to speak his mind. George had two brothers, Harry, and Bill. Bill Patton was a constable who had been killed in the line of duty. Harry had disappeared two years earlier. When asked where his brother went, George told the barber that Harry moved to California and he had not heard from him since. Now there were six people missing.

George was placed under custody and driven to Dallas, for questioning. Jess questioned George for three days, then had Sheriff Smoot Schmidt's two top investigators question the farmer for another three days.

"If George is lying," Smoot said, "His men will know in a another day or so."

Reporters anxiously waited for the results of the questioning, because if Patton confessed, it would be mass murder. It would be the crime of the decade.

The news hungry reporters from all major cities in Texas were ordered to hover over the Dallas jail like a buzzard over sick mule. Then, in the afternoon of the eighth day of questioning, Smoot's men met with the reporters.

"Gentlemen, after eight days of relentless questioning, we have been able to establish two things. Either George Patton is as innocent as a baby, or he is the best liar we've ever seen."

The interrogators doubted the farmer's story, but until some dead bodies showed up, George Patton was not going to trial.

Undeterred, Jess brought the farmer before a grand jury in Athens. He presented what evidence he had, and they questioned George for three hours before making their ruling: "Based on the evidence presented by Sheriff Sweeten of Henderson County, and the long hours of questioning in Dallas, Texas by the best interrogators in the state, we feel that the evidence presented to the Grand Jury by Sheriff Sweeten at this time is insufficient to bring this case to trial."

Richard returned Patton to his home. He explained to Patton why the case was impossible to prosecute without the *corpus delicti*. George said he understood that because he was an avid reader of all the detective magazines. Richard returned to Athens and publicly criticized the sheriff to the reporters.

"It seems that our Sheriff is barking up the wrong tree. As many of you know, there are approximately ten million people out of work in this country. Many have moved out to California trying to find employment. The McGehee's are just four of those ten million wandering souls."

Articles in the various publications seemed to lend credit to Richard's accusations. California was being flooded with so many refugees that armed patrols were turning them back. Many were shot while trying to enter the state illegally.

Jess and Hazel decided to walk to the cafe for a good breakfast. After walking two blocks, they met Will Henry walking toward them. Jess smiled at the old commissioner and said, "Good morning Mr. Henry."

Will stopped, looked hateful toward the couple, then quickly walked across the street to avoid the sheriff. Then as Jess and Hazel passed, he walked back across the street and continued on up the street.

Jess thought it odd, but figured Mr. Henry was just angry over the questioning of George Patton and wanted to show his displeasure. Will thought very highly of George. George was quick to share with his neighbors, and as far as Will Henry was concerned, Jess Sweeten could not hold George Patton a light to see by.

When they reached the end of the block, Jess noticed Harold Siglar engaged in a vicious argument with a telephone pole. Hazel said, "Jess you should tell Mrs. Siglar about Harold. He's as crazy as a bed bug."

Jess nodded and promised to tell her as soon as he had an opportunity.

Normally when he entered the cafe he was greeted warmly, but this time was different. A hush fell on the diners. Many cold stares greeted the once popular couple. Hazel noticed Mrs. Siglar at the back table so she escorted Jess to the front booth near the window.

They noticed Harold suddenly duck down as though the telephone pole had took a swing at him. Harold pulled out a pocket knife then took a swipe at the pole. Suddenly Richard Siglar appeared from around the corner and took the knife away from his brother. They fussed for a minute or so, then Harold walked away.

Richard walked to his mother's table and kissed her on the forehead.

"Sorry I'm late, mother. What did you order?"

She gave him a menu then said, "Richard, don't mention Jess Sweeten's name in front of Harold again."

"Okay, Mother! What are you going to order?"

"I mean it, Richard! you know what it does to him, and I'm not going to stand for it. Do you hear me?" "Yes, mother! Don't talk so loud. He's sitting right over there."

"I don't care, Richard...every time you mention his name, Harold gets so upset that I can't do anything with him!"

"Mother, I sent him home. Let's order."

Jess noticed Richard and his mother glaring hatefully. He excused himself and walked to Richard's table. He stood silently for a few moments, then quietly voiced his concern, "Mrs. Siglar, you need to have Harold examined. I've not bothered you about this. But for your own safety, please get that boy some help."

Richard's face turned the color of his hair. He stood shouting loud so that all could hear. "Sheriff, can't you see that we're trying to eat breakfast. Why in the hell do you keep butting in to our business?"

He took his mother by the arm, continuing to shout. "Come on, let's go some place where we can eat in peace!"

Jess noticed all eyes were focused in his direction. Hazel was very embarrassed. Jess knew she had lost her appetite, so he took her by the arm and they quietly walked out.

That afternoon, as Hazel shopped for jail groceries, Mrs. Davis and several other ladies whom she thought were good friends passed her in the produce aisle. Mrs. Davis pretended not to notice Hazel even though she had looked her right in the eye.

Hazel told Jess what had happened after they went to bed that night. She could not understand how people could be so two-faced. One minute they were well liked, and the next they were hated with a purple passion. Jess assured her that it was a well orchestrated defense ploy of Richard Sigler. He wanted to make Jess look foolish in public. And it would divert the attention away from his client, George Patton.

"What makes them believe George over you?" she asked seriously.

Jess pulled her face close, then kissed her on the forehead. "Do you love me?"

She kissed him passionately on the lips, then once over each eye.

"With all my heart."

"That's all that matters to me."

"But you didn't answer my question."

"Sugar, they don't have the information that I have. Sure they love ol' George now, but those same people will try to hang him when they learn the truth."

"But what if you can't prove it?"

Jess was silent for a long time. Hazel was right; if he failed to prove Patton was a mass murderer his career was over. And his name would be a joke on the lips of everyone in Henderson County.

"Jess, are you going to answer me?"

"Hazel, I gave my word that I'd find that family. If a man gives his word, he's made a debt. And I pay my debts."

"But we need to think about the future."

"What future would we have if my word didn't mean a hill of beans to those who place their faith in it?"

Hazel kissed him softly on the lips and whispered. "Jess, I'm pregnant."

Jess quickly leaned over with excitement, "You are! Are you sure?"

She began kissing him over the face with short pecks. "As sure as God made little green apples. Are you happy?"

"Yes, I'm happy!"

"What do you want, a boy or a girl?"

"I'll take what ever the good Lord sends our way."

***

Christmas, 1935 came and went. 1936 was ushered in with icy blasts of wind and rain. Then, on February fourth while Jess was sitting on the living room floor playing with his two year old daughter, Jessie Nell, Hazel read aloud from the paper.

"Listen to this, Jess," she said. "George Patton, age fifty-four, and a Miss Lorene Hawley, age sixteen, were married today in the office of Justice of the Peace, B.C. Hall."

This was a strange piece of news which came as a shock to Sweeten. He placed the baby in the crib, then sat silent on the sofa. If he didn't act quickly, Mrs. Patton would be dead within six months.

He decided to rattle the farmer's cage. Win or loose, he would strike one final blow!

At approximately one o'clock in the afternoon on the following spring day, February 28, 1936, Jess Sweeten tore the farmer's honeymoon all to pieces. When he arrived at the Sand Flat farm, George was repairing the wagon tongue. He was hammering the heel bolt and didn't hear the car drive into the front yard.

Lorene, the new bride, was washing the dinner dishes when Jess stepped out of the cruiser. Patton continued hammering the stubborn heel bolt with his back turned to the sheriff.

"Good afternoon, George," Jess hollered.

Astonished, Patton sprang to his feet and swung around violently with the hammer held tightly in his right hand. For a moment, Jess thought the farmer would throw the heavy hammer at him.

"Stay where you are, Sheriff!" Patton yelled.

"Put the damn hammer down, George!"

"I've had all this crap I'm going to put up with Sheriff!" Patton yelled to his wife. "Lorene! bring my rifle!"

Lorene ran out the back door toward George with a twelve gage shotgun in her hands.

Jess' mind raced. If he were forced to shoot the farmer, Richard Siglar would swear that it was murder. On top of that, he'd never find the missing McGehee family.

"Young lady! You stop right where you are!" Jess hollered.

"Woman! bring that damn rifle!" Patton shouted at the top of his lungs.

"Lorene! Stop or I'll kill him!" Jess hollered.

"George, I can't! He'll kill you!" she pleaded with her husband as she stopped in her tracks.

"Dammit, woman! Get that damn rifle over here!" Patton yelled.

Lorene walked another step toward her husband. Jess drew then aimed a forty-five automatic at Patton's head. Lorene took another two steps. Jess fired, knocking Patton's hat off his head.

"Young Lady!" Jess hollered. "If you take another step, I'll put a bullet right between his eyes!"

Lorene began to cry. She dropped the rifle to the ground and ran back into the house.

"Let's go, George!" Jess said calmly.

"Do you have a warrant for my arrest, Sheriff?"

"No, I don't George."

"Sheriff, Richard said you can't arrest me without a warrant."

"Yes I can, George. I'm bigger than he is. Now let's go."

"What about my wife?"

"She can go over to her mother's house."

"Where are you taking me?"

"You'll know when we get there."

George asked if he could change clothes before he left and Jess agreed that it would be a good idea. Lorene took a clean pair of pants off the clothes line as Jess emptied the shotgun. Within thirty minutes they were headed to Tyler, Texas.

The Smith County Sheriff prepared a room in the basement of the jail and promised that no attorney could find him there. Jess' car was hidden in a garage three blocks away. Before the questioning of Patton began, Jess called Texas Ranger Dan Hines and asked for his assistance in Henderson County.

Jess led Patton into the basement of the Tyler jail and began the questioning: "Take a seat over there George," Jess ordered as he took a seat opposite the farmer. They faced each other silently for several moments, each with a grim determination on his face. "Let's face the facts George. None of your stories hold water!"

"First you tell me that J. W. moved his family up to Oklahoma, then you concoct a story about a rift with the families of both Carrie and Johnny. Next, you tell me a fantastic story about shooting a house cat. You told that lie to explain the hole in the wall. Then I find that the pellets contained human blood. Next, we find a bloody shirt in a pile of brush that Mrs. Everett identified as belonging to Johnny McGehee. George, it baffles me how anyone could come up with such ridiculous lies about that evidence."

Jess placed the evidence on the long table.

Patton suddenly smiled. "Sheriff, in all my fifty-four years, I've never seen anybody as stubborn as you are."

"Well, George, coming from you that's a damn compliment. Because I feel the same way about you. And I know you're lying to me for a reason. We both know that those folks are dead. You know who killed them. Maybe it was you. Maybe it was someone else. But I feel confident that you're going to tell me the truth before we leave Tyler, Texas. It might take a week, two weeks or a month. But you'll tell me before we go back to Athens. That's a promise."

The questioning continued until late that afternoon. Suddenly George stretched his arms then yawned loudly.

"Sheriff, I'm hungry. Is there anything to eat around here?"

"What do you want?"

"I'd like a T-bone steak and a quart of milk."

Jess walked to Frogg's cafe, which was two blocks from the jail near the Joy theater. He ate a thick hamburger and a plate of french fries, then asked Frog to sack up a T-bone steak for the farmer. Within minutes, he returned to the jail basement and shoved the steak toward the hungry George Patton.

"Sheriff, do you reckon I could have a piece of pie to go with these groceries?"

"Hell, No!"

Patton ate the steak as though it was his last meal, then wiped his mouth with a slice of bread before downing the quart of milk.

"There, I feel much better now!"

Jess questioned Patton for three days and nights. The man consumed four T-bone steaks, a dozen eggs, a pound of bacon and two gallons of milk before he changed his story.

"George, are you about ready to me the truth?"

"Yeah, I guess it's about time."

"Alright. Let's start from the beginning."

"Well, Sheriff, I've lied long enough. And what I'm about to tell you is the gospel truth about it."

"Let's hear it."

"Did you know that J. W. was selling whiskey?"

"No, I didn't."

"Well, that's what cost him his life. What really happened was this: The two men that pulled up into the yard was bootleggers. The night they honked the horn, J. W. went out there just like I told you. J.

W. had beat them out of some money. I heard them out there in the yard arguing about it. It was two hundred dollars that he owed them, and what I mean, they come to collect! They hit J. W. a pretty good lick and he went down. Carrie ran out there and got right in the middle of it. One of those boys then took a swing at J. W. with a piece of pipe. I think it was a Ford axle but I'm not sure about that. Anyway, J. W. went down. When he went down, Carrie took to the house a runnin'. She grabbed up the kids and ran out the back door. The feller with the pipe was running after her. He caught her near the road and beat her to death. Bobby, the oldest boy lit out down the road. The other feller caught him. He took the boy by the legs and swung him around and around, then bashed his head against a large rock beside the road."

"Did you know those men?"

"No. I couldn't get a good look at them. It was too dark."

"Then what happened?"

"Well, when I got out of bed they seen me standing in the doorway. They tied a burlap sack over my head and took me out to the car. Then they shoved the bodies in the trunk and slammed the lid. They put me in the back seat and drove quite a distance from the farm, maybe five miles or so, and made me bury them. I couldn't see nothing. They said they'd kill me if I told anybody what they'd done. And the reason they let me live was because they didn't have nothing against me like they did with the McGehees."

"Then you can show me where they're buried?"

"I might, if you'll take me over there."

The farmer's story didn't make sense but at least this revelation would halt the filing of the *habeas corpus* by the Justice and Sigler law firm. Jess called Henderson County district attorney Miles B. Smith and asked him to take a formal statement from Patton. Smith drove to Tyler with a court stenographer and immediately took Patton's statement verbatim.

When the statement was completed, Patton signed document and Jess returned him to Athens. He placed Patton in a cell and ordered him to get a good night's sleep. They would start looking for the bodies early on the following morning.

Next day, March 5, 1936, Jess drove Patton to his home in Sand Flat. The search began at Patton's front yard. Jess backed the car out of the yard and asked him to point the way. He drove to the main dirt road near Chinquipin Ridge, then turned right. They continued past the graveyard for another half mile then suddenly Patton pointed toward a wagon rut road to the right.

"Turn here, Sheriff."

The road Patton identified was overgrown with high weeds. It was rough and full of ruts. He continued up the road for a mile or so. Then, just over the hill, Jess noticed a clearing, and the road became more visible, but it ended at a large, newly constructed stock pond some five hundred yards farther.

"George, are you sure that we're headed in the right direction?"

"Sheriff, they're buried somewhere out in middle of that lake."

"What the hell are you trying to tell me, George?"

"Sheriff, that lake wasn't here in 1932. Somebody's dammed up the creek. I'm sure this is the right place."

Jess returned Patton to his cell.

Through the objections of the man who owned the property, Jess received a court order to have the lake drained. Then, after several more weeks, the ground had dried enough to began the digging.

Patton took the shovel from Sweeten's car then walked a short distance away and began digging. Jess stood a short distance away observing the farmer's work. Within six hours, Patton had dug a hole approximately four feet across and eight feet deep. The man was digging a well. Sweeten allowed George to continue digging through the red clay earth until he could no longer throw the dirt out.

By allowing Patton to do this, Jess gained valuable information without the farmer knowing. The bodies, if they were ever located, were buried deep under ground. And from this first hole, Jess knew George was stalling for time. A time when Jess would no longer be the Henderson County sheriff. He would have to press the farmer much harder.

Jess walked to the edge of the hole, intending to give George a good tongue lashing. But after thinking it over, he decided to be patient. "George, we're digging at the wrong location."

"Sheriff, I think you're right."

"Well, come on out of there. We'll try again tomorrow."

Within a month, George Patton had dug up half of Henderson County. He had dug no less than twenty holes within five miles of the Patton farm. It was like a never ending Easter egg hunt. Patton dug with enthusiasm during the day, and with flood-lights during the night. Jess

116

pressed harder. Each digging session grew longer and longer—up to fourteen hours a day. By God, he'd make that farmer wish he'd never seen a shovel! But the old man continued digging holes and eating T-bone steaks without a single complaint about the hard work. George Patton was a tough old bird.

The last hole was nearing completion in the late afternoon of July 13th. Patton had again dug to a depth of approximately seven feet when Jess stepped atop of the huge mound of dirt. He was tired and flustered at the stalling tactics of the farmer. He pulled the pistol from the holster, then took aim at Patton's head.

"That's deep enough George."

"Sheriff! What are you going to do?"

"I'm going to blow your dammed head off, George. Then I'm going to cover you up."

"Sheriff, you can't do that. I'm trying my best."

"No, you're not, George. You're betting that I won't be re-elected, and you could be right. So I'll just end it right here."

"But, Sheriff, I'm doing the best I can."

"Where are the bodies, George?"

"Sheriff, I'm racking my brains trying to help. You got to protect me."

Jess fired bullets all around the farmer, causing him to tremble with fear.

"You killed the McGehees, George! Now, where did you bury them?"

George began to cry. He slumped down in the hole, covering his head with both hands.

"Please, Sheriff. You've got to believe me."

Jess leaned over and grabbed the farmer by the arm and pulled him from the hole. The digging stopped. Jess had to begin campaigning for a third term if he intended to continue the investigation.

Using the same ink blotter literature, Jess Sweeten easily won a third term as Sheriff of Henderson County.

During this time, he was extremely busy trying to solve another murder case in the Stoddard community, near Athens, and was out of town quite a bit. Clyde Barrow and Bonnie Parker had captured the public's attention. Roosevelt's second "New Deal" was underway. The Tennessee Valley Authority had became a huge success in helping put America back to work. Humorist, Will Rogers was quoted as saying, "I will say one thing for this administration. It's the only time when a fellow with money is worrying more than the one without it."

***

On September 25, 1936, Hazel had planned to pack a lunch and take her husband fishing. She figured Jess needed to take his mind off the two murder cases he had been working at the same time. He needed to spend time with his daughter.

Jess wanted to fish a spot on the Trinity River about two miles south of Trinidad near the cliffs. The place where the old abandoned Cotton storage building used to stand. Years earlier, when he was constable of Trinidad, a fellow named Albert Woolfe told him about the area. Albert caught big catfish down there. Albert and his wife Thelma supplemented a meager farm income by selling catfish to several restaurants up in Dallas. Then, during the winter, they'd sell hot tamales in many towns throughout the county. Albert's secret spot for fishing was located somewhere between those bluffs and the old Airheart Ferry.

Hazel spread the blanket in an open area because Jess wanted her to be on the look out for Albert. That way, he could guarantee them good supper. He knew if he was unsuccessful, Albert would surely give him a few. He baited two hooks and led his daughter to the bank of the wide river.

Hazel watched silently, noticing the patience of her husband— realizing the pain she would suffer if she lost either. And her thoughts wandered to Florence Everett, a woman who would never again know such pleasures. She watched baby Jessie's successful attempt at capturing her father's undivided attention for over an hour. And it was fun to watch them play until the baby fell asleep in her father's massive arms.

Minutes later, Jess noticed Albert and his heavy-set wife walking toward the river. Albert didn't notice the sheriff nor his family watching from the distance. He baited a hook, then cast his line in the water. And no sooner than his hook hit bottom, Albert jerked his pole backward and pulled in a whopper. Jess watched as the big jolly. Albert placed his fish on a stringer, then threw the thing back in the water and pulled in another large catfish.

118

In less than ten minutes, Albert had a full stringer of approximately seven medium sized channel-cat. It was unfair for one man to have that kind of knowledge of fish without sharing the secret. Jess placed the baby next to Hazel, then walked over to Mr. and Mrs. Albert Woolfe's lucky spot.

"Thelma, looky who's a here!" Albert hollered in a high pitched, snuff-dipping voice.

"Morning, Albert, Thelma. Any luck?"

Albert lifted his large stringer of catfish.

"Oh, I can't complain, Jess. How bout you?"

"I had a nibble about an hour ago. That's about it."

"Well, my goodness, Sheriff. What kind of bait ye' using?"

"Oh. I've got a can of Georgia wigglers over there. What kind of bait do you have?"

Albert opened a the lid on a quart-size mason jar releasing a foul odor which caused Jess to take several steps backward.

"Skunk bags!" Albert said in his high pitched tone.

"I set traps fer skunks. Then I operate on their little stink bags. An' 'en I sell 'em fer pets. Hit takes me about two weeks to get me a jar full."

"Albert!" yelled Thelma, "put the lid back on that jar! You're stinking up the whole neighborhood!" She walked a few yards up the bank holding her nose. A Negro family who had been fishing twenty-five yards down wind from Albert quickly packed up and moved farther down stream.

"I don't think I could get use to that!" Jess said, covering his mouth and nose with his hand.

"Oh! you get use to anything after a while," Albert blurted with a deep belly laugh—spilling half a lipful of snuff. He lifted the jar to his nose and sniffed the foul aroma as though it were a bottle of three dollar perfume. He baited another hook, then turned toward Jess with a serious look.

"Sheriff, can I ask you a question?"

"Sure."

"Is ye' still after ol' George Patton?"

Jess stepped closer to the fisherman after he got the lid back on the jar.

"Yes, I am, Why?"

Thelma butted in before Albert could speak. "We bought a mattress from George. We paid five hard-earned dollars for that thang, and when we got it home, it had a big ol' stain of blood all over the bottom side!"

Jess became very curious. "What portion of the mattress? Was it near the middle, or at he end?"

"Hit was at the end of the mattress," Albert interrupted, "I didn't notice that stain when I bought it off of him 'cause George put it in the truck. He had the good side turned up. But when I got it home and Thelma took a look at it—she throwed herself a little hissy-fit."

"Yes, I did, Sheriff! And I had a good cause to do it. I told Albert I wanted my money back. But Ol' Easy didn't want to cause no trouble about it. Five dollars! Just throwed down a rat hole!"

"Do you still have the mattress?"

"Yeah. Hit's out there in the barn."

"If you'll bring it to my office, I'll pay you the five dollars."

After the picnic, Jess showed Patton the bloody mattress.

"George, you sold this mattress to Albert Woolfe. He took it home and look what he finds on the other side. This large stain of blood. What happened here?" Why did you sell it?"

"Yes, I can explain that stain. It had too many bad memories."

"Bad memories?"

"Yes. That's the mattress my brother Bill died on. He was a constable. He went to arrest, Ned Corbitt. Ned ambushed him from under the porch. Bill died on that mattress."

"He died at your house?"

"No. He died at his house."

"How did the mattress wind up at your house?"

"I inherited some of his things."

"Why did you sell a useless mattress? They tell me you're an honest man."

"Sheriff, that mattress cost my brother ten dollars. It was good on one side. So I sold it for five."

Jess continued questioning Patton all that night and half the next day before Attorney Richard Sigler appeared with a *habeas corpus*. He stormed into the interrogation room in a fit of rage.

"Sheriff! do you intend to charge my client with a crime?"

"No, but if I do, Richard, you'll be the first to know!"

"Then may I take him home?"

"That won't be necessary, Richard. I brought him here and I'll take him home."

Jess loaded the farmer in his car and drove George to the farm and asked him to make a pot of coffee. After they had drank several cups, Jess ordered George to get in the car.

"Sheriff, Richard has papers saying you got to let me go."

"Yes, he does. Those papers were filed in Henderson County. We're going to Van Zandt County, and unfortunately for you, those papers are no good up there."

The questioning continued for three days before Richard Sigler could find him. But before attorney Sigler could file a new *habeas corpus* with the Van Zandt County authorities, Jess had taken George to Waxahachie. When Richard found him in Waxahachie, Jess drove him to Palestine.

While in Palestine, Jess fished during the daytime, and questioned Patton at night. But Richard Sigler was a darn good attorney. He petitioned for and received a *habeas corpus* in each of the surrounding counties then ordered a constable to locate and serve Jess Sweeten no matter what county he happened to be at the time.

Jess was served in Palestine, Texas. George Patton returned to Athens looking as though he had been beaten. Dark circles had formed around Patton's eyes. Richard was furious. He asked George if Jess had beat him while in custody. George pitifully looked toward his attorney and said, "Well, a little more than I could stand."

The lie that George told his attorney stirred a hornet's nest. Jess lost a good many more of his supporters. Richard had Patton examined by a doctor. The doctor stated that Patton could have been beaten during questioning but he could find no evidence that a beating had actually occurred.

According to Henderson County officials, Jess Sweeten was out of control. A meeting was called at the courthouse, and Jess was ordered to appear before the court. Will Henry broke the icy silence.

"Jess, everybody in Henderson County knows that George Patton is innocent except you! Why, he's the most decent, honest man I've ever known and you're trying to kill him. He's a human being for Christ's sake! And you're treating the man like a damn dog! You ought to be ashamed of yourself!"

Mrs. Davis butted in. "Jess, up until now you've made us a pretty good Sheriff. But you've lost your cotton picking mind over this Patton thing. Why, if George owed you a dime, he'd walk ten miles to pay you back! He's the most honest man you'll ever meet in your life..."

Jess interrupted. "Yes, Mrs. Davis! I'm sure that George Patton is an honest man! But he's also a cold-bloodied murderer! I don't know how I can prove it to you, Mrs. Davis. I may never prove it. But, by damn, I'm going to try! Just let me have him for two weeks without those *habeas corpus* flying everywhere and I might have a chance to prove it!"

Richard Sigler jumped into the fray. "Two weeks...Hell! You've had three years! You took him down there and beat him half to death! What are you trying to do, kill him?" I won't stand for it!"

"Richard, I've never laid a hand on George Patton."

Will Justice spoke up. "Jess, let's be reasonable about this. You know that a man will confess to anything if you pressure him hard enough. Any man will crack if enough pressure is applied. Guilty or not. The statement George gave you was made under that type of pressure. I don't believe that statement for one minute. So, what other evidence do you have?"

"Will, I have enough evidence to convince me that George Patton is a murderer."

"Sheriff, the evidence you gathered was all circumstantial, and the grand jury threw it out."

"Let me ask you something, Will. If I could prove that Patton was a cold-blooded murderer beyond the shadow of a doubt, would you still defend him?"

"No, I'd prosecute him. But, Jess, you're wrong about George Patton!"

"Then, let me have him for two weeks."

"No!" Sigler shouted, "because you'll take him off some place and beat a confession out of that poor man!"

"Richard, I've never laid a hand on a prisoner in my life, and you know that!"

"You beat George Patton!"

"That's a damn lie, Richard!"

"You took a belt to Travis Moore!"

"Travis beat his wife! And I warned the man five times before I took a belt to him."

"What about the man over in Malakoff?" Richard shouted,"You hit him so hard he was in a coma for a week!"

"Well, he challenged me to a fair fist-fight and when I got over there he came at me with a machine hammer."

Will Henry spoke up. "Everybody knows you're just using that old man to keep your name in all the papers."

Jess angrily stormed out of the court room.

Next morning, Lorene Patton, walked into Richard's office with her father, T. E. Hawley. She reported that Jess Sweeten had drove out to the Patton farm in the middle of the night and took George away. Richard angrily walked to the sheriff's office and found a Texas Ranger named Dan Hines sitting behind Jess' desk. He demanded to know the whereabouts of his client George Patton. Dan told him that Jess had not told him where he was headed. Only that he would be back in about two weeks.

While Jess and Patton waged a furious mental battle, Richard Sigler was forming a plan to lure him from his hiding place. An insurance salesman told Richard that his company carried the sheriff's insurance policy. The premium was four days late. Richard asked the man to call Hazel and ask to speak with the sheriff. He figured she'd knew where Jess was holed up.

"Mrs. Sweeten, this is urgent," said the insurance salesman. "I need to speak with Jess. It's very important that I see him immediately. It's about his insurance policy."

"He's not here."

"Mrs. Sweeten, I must meet with Jess today. His premium is in arrears. He must bring the money in person. The company that I represent is threatening cancellation."

"I'll try to locate him. How much do we owe?"

"Thirty dollars."

It was not true that Hazel didn't know Jess' whereabouts. She asked Dan Hines to call Jess immediately.

Meanwhile, the stress was getting to George Patton. He had not slept in eight days and nights. George had begun to act silly from his lack of sleep, and each question was being answered with laughter. Suddenly, George turned to the Sheriff and said, "Sheriff, did you know that human flesh will boil off the bones quicker than beef?"

"What are you saying George?"

"Oh! It's a fact."

"A fact about what?"

"Sheriff, I've been laughing about that for over three years! Yes, I killed the McGehee's. Do you remember the oil drums that those ladies rolled under the shade tree? Remember? They made a table out of them!"

"Yes, I remember. What about them?"

"Well, I put J. W. and Doyle's body in one barrel, and Carrie and Bobby's body in the other. Then I built a log heap around each barrel and boiled the meat off their bones. It took me about two hours. Then I built me another fire and burned the meat to cinders!"

"What did you do with the bones?"

"I went to the barn, got me a hammer and busted them in little pieces. Then I threw them into the fire and burned them up."

At this news, Jess walked slowly down the hall to the kitchen. He poured himself a cup of coffee, then sat silent at the table in deep meditation until Sheriff Sykes told him he had an urgent phone call from Athens.

"Hello. This is Sheriff Sweeten."

"Jess, this is Dan. Hazel wants to talk to you."

"Yes, Sugar?"

"Jess, I hate to bother you, but your insurance premium is due. The man said if he didn't have the money today, it would be canceled. What do you want me to do?"

"I forgot all about that. But don't worry. I'll go to the bank and borrow some money. I'll see you in forty-five minutes."

"What about George?"

"I'm placing him under arrest for murder."

"He confessed!"

"Yes. About five minutes ago."

Jess placed Patton under arrest, then asked Sheriff Sykes guard his prisoner. He figured that Richard was behind the insurance problem, so he quickly drove toward Athens.

Within thirty minutes of the phone call, Richard stormed into the Smith County jail demanding Patton's release.

"You can't have him," said Sheriff Sykes. "He's under arrest for murder."

Jess arrived in Athens a few minutes ahead of schedule then drove straight to the bank which was full of last minute depositors. He quickly walked to the loan officer's desk and said, "Luther, I need to borrow thirty dollars."

Luther placed his hands behind his head, then leaned proudly backward in his fancy hand carved chair. Luther had a smirk on his face.

"Thirty dollars, huh?" Luther asked in a rather loud voice which caused several patrons to look his way.

"Yes, sir. Thirty dollars even."

Luther smiled a wolfish grin toward the man in the next office, then shuffled a small stack of papers on his desk, savoring the moment before giving his loud answer.

"Jess, I can't loan you thirty dollars!"

"What are you talking about, Luther? I've borrowed money from this bank before."

"Well, you're a bad risk!"

"A bad risk?"

"Well, it's getting close to election time and you'll be out of a job. How would you be able to pay me back?"

Jess' first reaction was to reach across the desk and slap the grin off Luther's face, but he held his temper in check. Without another word the embarrassed sheriff gritted his teeth and walked toward the door.

As Jess opened the large oak door, Luther shouted so loud that the whole bank could hear: "Jess! When are you going to leave George Patton alone? Don't you think you've had enough publicity off that poor man?"

The banker's words cut like a knife. Luther had embarrassed him in front of the bank. Jess quickly turned around and walked back to Luther's desk. "Luther, you and your friends have given me hell over George Patton for three years. You've run all over this county telling everybody how innocent he is! But I'll promise you one damn thing! Before the sun goes down, I'll show you what a fool you've been!"

Sheriff Jess Sweeten stormed out of the bank. He was refused the loan and his insurance policy was canceled. He continued on to the Patton farm. Patton's wife, Lorene, was hanging clothes on the line. Jess walked directly to the two oil drums near the barn and examined them very carefully. Lorene cautiously walked up behind him nervously wringing her hands.

"Sheriff, where's George?"

"Lorene, your husband has been charged with murder. He's being held in the Smith County jail. If you wish, you can have your daddy

Sheriff Jess Sweeten of Henderson County, Tex., examines big drums in which George Patton is said to have boiled down the flesh of four murder victims.

drive you down there to visit with him."

"Well, what are you looking for?"

"I need to take a look around. I won't be long."

Jess ran his hand around the rim of the barrel. Both had a greasy substance that covered the upper inside portion. *Could this substance be the only remains of the McGehee family.* Jess took a closer look. Not at the substance, but at the barrels themselves. Something was wrong with Patton's story.

He returned to Athens and had supper with Hazel and his daughter, then called Miles Smith, the District Attorney, and told him to take a court stenographer to Tyler for a second statement from George.

When Jess returned to Tyler, a host of reporters met him on the front steps of the red brick jail house. He answered their questions until District Attorney Smith and his stenographer showed up.

"Are you ready, George?" Jess asked.

"Yes, it's like I said. I killed J. W. but it was self defense."

"Self defense?"

"Yes."

"Just start from the beginning, George."

"Alright, Sheriff. This here is the way it really happened! J.W. went off and was gone an hour or two, and he came back and was drinking. We fed and tended to things and went to bed that night. Him and his wife, she was laying on the little bed, and me, I was laying on the mattress and springs on the floor, and they talked about they would finish shelling the corn the next day.

"He said he would finish it up, and the next day he wouldn't do nothing; he just pottered about there. When we ate our supper that night, why, I told him I believed we should go and turn the cows and yearlings and mules out.

"We got up and started out and smoked a cigarette as we were going. Her, Mrs. McGehee, and the children followed us out there. I fastened up my chickens and went in the hall of the barn to turn my mules out, and I said to him, 'I wish you would finish shelling this corn and pay me what you said you would do.' He owed me a little better than twenty dollars. I had loaned him some money to buy groceries and some medicine before he come there; that's why he moved there, and he wanted to get the corn out there where he could sell it. I don't remember what the next words were that he said.

"He never did tell me who he was going to sell the corn to. You could take a car of it and in an hour's time you could be in Van Zandt or somewhere; I don't know who he was going to sell it to. He said to me he wasn't going to do a G-D-thing, and right then he struck at me; he struck with his fist, and I dodged it and we had it round and round. I struck at him and hit him on the side of the neck, and he then struck me and knocked me down and back about ten feet.

"As I was getting up he made at me and I got up and got an iron pipe. When I turned around he had one in his hand. We struck at one another, and Carrie, she run in between us, and I don't know which of us hit her, him or me. We were both striking at one another and she fell between us.

"He hit me on the side of the neck and knocked me down. He made for me and I got up. I hit him and staggered him. He got up and clinched me, and got me down and was choking me, and I run my hand up to his face and got one finger in his eye. I gave him a pull and he turned over sideways and I got up.

"One of the pieces of iron we had was close by and I got up and struck at him, and I hit the biggest boy through a mistake hitting at him. Then I hit Johnny two or three licks. The next thing I remember I was sitting on my doorsteps.

"I decided I would come in to the law, and I said to myself, 'no that won't do because his biggest brothers would kill me, I'll just figure a way to get shed of everything.

"I rolled them two oil drums that me and Mrs. Nobles used to make some lye soap with to the back of the house. I made a log heap around each barrel, then I put J. W. and the youngest boy in one barrel, and Carrie and the oldest boy in the other barrel.

"I cooked them for about two hours until the meat slipped off the bones, then I built another fire and burned the meat. Some of the bones wouldn't burn, so I went to the barn and got a hammer. I broke the bones in little pieces and then I burned them again. I scattered the cinders in the yard."

After receiving a copy of Patton's statement, three Tyler newspapermen took it upon themselves to drive to Henderson County and sift Patton's yard for bones. They sifted several hundred yards of dirt for three hours, then drove to the sheriff's office and proudly turned over fifteen fragments of what appeared to be human bone.

Jess called Dr. Henderson to his office at nine thirty the following morning to examine the fragments. Dr. Henderson used a large volume of medical pictures to make comparisons, and said that one of the fragments resembled the pelvis socket of a child, another resembled a piece of skull. A third fragment was described as probably being a shoulder or hip-bone fragment. He declined to positively identify the bones as being those of a human being, placing emphasis on the word "resembled."

The Tyler men told Sheriff Sweeten that they secured the bone fragments at the scene of an old fire near the Patton house, at the spot where the accused man said that he boiled the bodies before burning the bones and flesh. They reported that many more fragments were seen lying about the same spot.

T. E. Hawley, the father of Patton's sixteen-year-old bride, appeared at the Sheriff's office when the fragments were being examined and said, "You can pick up barrels of bones about the farm where Patton has slaughtered cattle and hogs. These bones look too bleached-out to have been covered with earth in recent months."

While waiting on the report from Austin, Patton's wife Lorene, her father and Richard Sigler paid a visit to the haggard looking George Patton. His eyes were ringed with dark circles which appeared to have been blackened by blows to the face. Richard was furious. The farmer had lost at least ten pounds during the last questioning.

"George," said Sigler, "What happened to you? Did Jess beat you while you were in his custody?"

"Well, it was a little more than I could stand."

"How many times has he beat you George?"

"In the past three years?"

"Yes. How many times?"

"About a dozen times."

"George, this is very important. What about those bones that were found in your yard?"

"Richard, you can go to any farm in the county and find bones in the yard. Chicken bones, hog bones, cow bones...all kinds of bones."

"The bones they found in your yard, what kind of bones are they?"

"More than likely hog bones. I've killed lots of hogs over the years."

Richard angrily told the reporters gathered on the steps of the Tyler jail that Patton's statement was false. "Sheriff Sweeten bludgeoned a confession out of my client, as he has done on many other occasions."

"Then you believe that Mr. Patton confessed in order to stop those beatings?"

"Yes, I do. Mr. Patton has lost ten pounds while in the custody of Sheriff Sweeten. He has been beaten and starved to the point of being near death. Sheriff Sweeten has absolutely no regard for law and order whatsoever. He is a bully who seeks only publicity for himself. And it is clear to me that we must change our laws to protect innocent people from these thugs with badges."

"What about the bones found on the Patton farm?" asked one reporter.

"My client is innocent, and those bones will prove it once and for all!" Richard shouted.

"But," said the reporter, "the Henderson County coroner himself said the bones, in his opinion, were human."

"You just wait," Richard said with a smile, "My client has told the truth from the very start of this case."

"Are you saying that the sheriff is lying?"

"Well, let's wait and see."

"Do you think Jess Sweeten is a liar?"

"Those bones will prove he is lying about my client.

Late that afternoon, Jess received a call from a dance hall near the southern edge of the county. A drunk had been caught in the parking lot siphoning gasoline from parked automobiles. When confronted, the drunk began making threats and the owner of the establishment was afraid it would end with a killing.

Hazel had not spent much time with her husband in the past few months, so she decided to go with him. She walked up to a second floor cell and got the baby who had been left in the care of a prisoner. The one good thing about living in an apartment in the jail was the fact that Hazel had a never ending supply of free baby-sitters. And it taught responsibility to the prisoners.

The two lane highway in the southern part of the county had a lot of hills and valleys. Branches of the trees extended over the highway in that area making it seem as though they were traveling through a tunnel.

Meanwhile, the drunk sped toward Athens like a bat out of hell. He had a full tank of gas and was weaving all over the road. Both cars met at the top of the hill. The drunk had failed to turn his lights on. Baby Jessie Nell went through the front windshield and landed somewhere in the ditch beside the road.

When the two cars came to a stop, the upper portion of Hazel's body rested on the hood of the cruiser while her lower portion remained wedged between the seat and dashboard. Her face was a bloody mess and all her teeth were missing. Jess suffered wounds to his chest and face but quickly tore the door off the car to get to his wife. She was alive and begging him to find the baby.

Miraculously, the drunk crawled through the window of his overturned car unscathed. Jess frantically ordered the man to help search for baby Jessie Nell who lay somewhere beside the road. Within seconds, Jess found his daughter laying in the ditch some fifty feet from the accident. She was covered in blood. Large slivers of glass were protruding through her jaw, face and chin. The entire left side of baby Jessie Nell's cheek had been cut from lip to ear. The huge gash was pouring blood. A multitude of other cuts on the left side of her face were filled with bits of gravel and dirt. But she was breathing.

Jess sat down in the ditch, took his daughter in his arms. He pressed her face tightly to stop the bleeding, then rocking back and forth...pleading with God to let his daughter live. Through tears streaming down his eyes, he noticed a car speeding up the road toward the accident. He shouted for the drunk to flag it down as Hazel limped to the ditch to be with her husband and daughter.

The drunk frantically waved his arms while standing in the center of the road refusing to budge an inch. The man almost got himself run over but at the last minute was able to get the drivers attention.

Baby Jessie Nell Sweeten was taken to a Dallas hospital where her wounds were temporarily stitched together. The doctor warned Jess that she would endure years of plastic surgery in order to gain even a partial resemblance to her former self. Hazel had lost all her teeth in the accident but she was fitted with a new set after her wounds healed.

The report concerning bone fragments found in the yard of Patton's home reached Jess' desk three days after the accident. It contained more bad news. All the bone fragments were found to be animal bones. Richard Sigler was elated over this news. While he celebrated with the Hawley family, Jess quietly returned to the Tyler jail to began another round of relentless questioning of George Patton.

"George, did you cut the bodies up before you put them in the barrels?"

"No, I didn't. I just put them in the barrels and filled them up with water."

"Then your whole damn statement is a lie George. You didn't burn those bodies. You buried them!"

"Sheriff, I told the truth about what I done to them. And it was done in self defense."

"How tall was J. W. McGehee George!"

"He was at least six foot."

"George, a fifty-five gallon oil drum stands exactly thirty-four and one-half inches tall from the bottom rim to the top. That's less than three feet. There is no way you could have put two bodies in either one of those drums without chopping them all to pieces."

"I didn't have no trouble at all getting them in there. I just bent his legs back and set him in there. Then I got me a cedar post and propped it under his chin while his bottom part cooked."

"Was the post on the inside or the outside the barrel?"

"It was on the outside of the barrel."

"You had a fire going around the barrel George! The dammed cedar post would have burned up!"

Jess continued questioning Patton all that night, then at approximately 11 o'clock the following morning he was relieved by Texas Ranger Dan Hines and Dick Olden. They continued questioning Patton in shifts of fourteen hours each. This time, Jess had a doctor present throughout the questioning. Day after day Jess questioned the farmer. He was allowed only three hours sleep each day. The questioning lasted for fourteen days before Patton threw up his hands. "Sheriff. I've had all this I can take! Just take me home and I'll dig them up!"

As Jess and Dan drove toward the Patton farm, Jess turned to the farmer and said, "George, since you've confessed to killing them, now tell me how and why you killed them."

Patton silently looked out the window for a long time before he spoke. "J. W. and me got in an argument. We were supposed to split the corn fifty-fifty. Johnny accused me of taking more than my share. We commenced to fight about it. He was a lot bigger than me. I was no match for him. So I knocked him in the head with a piece of two-inch pipe. It was an iron pipe, and was about three foot long.

"While we were fighting, Carrie ran up between us just as I was swinging the pipe at Johnny again. The pipe hit her in the head instead of J. W. and she fell to the ground. I guess it killed her. Then I hit J. W. again, and that finished him off. After that, I looked at Carrie there on the ground and began to feel pitiful about what I had done because I hadn't realized that she had the baby in her arms.

132

"The baby boy was just laying beside her mother, dead. That was an accident of hitting her and the baby. Then the oldest boy took to running all around the yard and screaming about it. Then, all of a sudden, he lit out down the road. I studied and studied as what to do about it, then I realized he'd go off somewhere and tell. So I took out after him. And I caught him about halfway down the road and dragged him back to the house. I was dragging him by both his legs and he never did shut his mouth. I told him to shut up that screaming, but no, he was screaming at the top of his lungs. You could hear him for five miles.

"Then I seen a rock sticking out of the bank beside the road, and I told him to shut up again. He wouldn't do it. I told him I'd bash his head in if he didn't. I'd never heard such squalling in all my life. So, I swung him round and round by the legs then bashed his head into that big rock beside the road."

"What did you do then?"

"Well, It was late in the afternoon the day before Thanksgiving in 1932 when we had the fight. And I knew that Carrie's mother was coming over to pick them up the next day, so I took me a shovel from the barn and dug a hole behind the house. There was a lot of roots there so I tried another spot. I was lucky on the next try. Well, I dug the hole and then I tied a rope around Johnny's neck and dragged him out there to the hole. I left the rope around his neck. Then I dragged Carrie and the kids to the hole. The rock that was sticking out from the bank had a lot of blood on it, so I threw it in the hole with them. I threw the pipe in the hole too."

They pulled into the yard of Patton's Sand Flat farm. When George got out of the car, Lorene ran to greet him. A number of cars began driving toward the farm as George and Lorene kissed. George looked longingly toward the farm as if it would be the last time. More cars were coming up the road.

"Lorene, go on over to your mother's house," said the farmer solemnly. "I'm going to dig up the bodies."

"George! What are you talking about?"

She pulled away from her husband before the reporter snapped the picture.

George Patton admitting murders to his wife

"Just go on over to your mother's...I've had all I can take. The sheriff is killing me with all them damn questions. I just can't take it any more." He patted the stomach of his pregnant wife and said, "I don't want you and the baby to see this."

Lorene immediately began walking down the road toward her mother's house as another two cars pulled into the yard. Patton waited until Lorene was out of sight then walked directly to the barn. He took a hammer and straightened the lip of the shovel, then opened the wooden gate and began to dig between the gate posts.

The gate?

Jess angrily walked to the farmer and said, "Damn you, George! We dug here! You saw us dig here! We went down six feet!"

George stopped digging momentarily. There was strange smile was on his face. "Yes, and I was sitting over there on the steps praying that you wouldn't go deep enough and you didn't. They're eight feet down."

George Patton digging for bodies　　　　*Photo by R.T. Craig*
Left to Right-Jess Sweeten Ranger, Dan Hines, George Patton

When the hole had reached a depth of seven feet, Dan Hines walked up to Jess then squatted down near the rim. He turned to the anxious sheriff and said, "Jess, do you think he's telling the truth this time?"

"I don't know, Dan. He's been lying for four years..."

At that moment several hand bones flew from the deep hole between the gate posts and landed beside Jess' boot. He examined them carefully as George stopped to rest.

"Sheriff, they're down here somewhere."

"Come on out, George. I think you've found them."

Jess showed the bones to R. T. Craig, who was holding a new flashlight operated camera toward the trio. He helped the farmer out of the hole then ordered several other men to complete the digging.

The first body recovered was that of the two-year-old Bobby McGehee. It had been carefully wrapped in an army blanket, and placed on top of his mother. The body was clothed in a torn shirt and overalls. There were no wounds to the skull as George said. In the right hand pocket of the boy's overalls Jess found four acorns. And for some reason those acorns caused him to choke up.

Jess gripped the acorns tightly in his fist then walked away from the crowd. The sun had gone down. He leaned over the fence and gazed toward the darkness of the woods...and tears flowed freely.

Suddenly, as the body of the other boy was pulled from the grave, Jess heard a man from the crowd curse loudly at the farmer. Jess recognized the voice. It was Luther.

"You're a son of a bitch, George!" Luther hollered.

"Let's hang the bastard right here!" shouted another.

Patton quickly walked away from the crowd, toward the big sheriff and said, "Sheriff, you promised to stand by me."

Jess wiped his eyes, then angrily turned toward the advancing crowd and said, "Yes, and I intend to do just that!" He pointed his finger toward the crowd: "I'll kill the first man that tries to take you!"

He quickly loaded Patton in his car then drove him to Palestine and lodged Patton in the Anderson County jail.

George Patton, the honest farmer, was formally charged with murder. His Sand Flat shanty now stood empty and deserted. On March 17, 1936, Patton was returned to the Henderson County jail where his confession was taken by Attorney Miles B. Smith. Patton signed the paper with a sigh of relief that the whole ordeal was over.

The sheriff's office was besieged with mountains of letters from all over the country. Reporters from as far away as Chicago and New York City filled the small town of Athens, Texas. Another avalanche of letters poured in from Europe. Scotland Yard called to congratulate the determined lawman. Every magazine in the country wanted stories and pictures of the famous "Boy Sheriff."

Judge Ben Dent impaneled a grand jury to investigate the Patton case, and after several hours of deliberation, returned four indictments against the Sand Flat farmer. The trial was set for July 1936. When the case came to trial, Richard Sigler pleaded for a change of venue. The case had caused so much publicity that he felt Patton could not get a fair trial in Henderson County.

Fearing a reversal from the Court of Criminal Appeals the change of venue was granted, and the trial was moved to Waxahachie, Ellis County, Texas. The trial was set for November, 1936.

As he had promised earlier, Will Justice was appointed special prosecutor in the case. Though the farmer was a friend of Will Justice, no defendant was more vigorously prosecuted. Patton was charged with only one count —the murder of Carrie McGehee, since her skull was more easily identified than the others. The trial lasted for four days and the jury returned a verdict of guilty.

While awaiting his trip to Huntsville, Patton learned that Lorene, his wife, had given birth to a son. The boy was born dead nine o'clock the Monday following the trial.

Three weeks before the electrocution, Patton sent word to Sheriff Sweeten that he wanted to tell where he buried the bodies of Nellie Phillips and his brother, Harold. But on his arrival at Huntsville, the priest who had been comforting the farmer refused permission. "Sheriff, I've been preparing the man to meet his maker, and after three days I think he is ready. If you go in there, he'll become upset and I'll have to prepare him all over again. All you will have is another pile of bones. I can't stop you sheriff, but please let the man die in peace."

George Patton bravely walked to the electric chair one minute after midnight on July, 30, 1943. The priest asked if he had any last words. George smiled and said, "I hope we are all forgiven for our sins." He waived to the crowd of twenty-eight spectators. Fifteen minutes later, George Patton was pronounced dead. He was buried in the prison cemetery.

In some ways, the farmer had won his battle with the sheriff. He had lied to the very end. The real story of what happened on the Patton farm that day before Thanksgiving in 1932 went to the grave with him. Later, Jess offered his theory of the events at the Patton farm:

"J. W. had used Patton's wagon to haul the corn to Van Zandt County, leaving Patton alone with Carrie and the two boys. They all lived together in that two room shack. And I believe the farmer was smitten with J. W's young wife. Anyway, at some point during the day, Patton forced himself on Carrie McGehee. And when she threatened to tell her husband, Patton killed her with the pipe. She apparently died on the mattress. The part of Patton's story about Doyle proved to be true. He had chased the boy down the road, dragged him by the legs to the side of the road, then swung him around, bashing his head against the rock. After killing Carrie and Doyle, Patton waited for the return of Johnny McGehee. When J. W. walked into the room and found his wife dead on the mattress, Patton charged from the other room with the shotgun. He blasted J. W. against the wall. After the grave was dug, Patton placed the three bodies in the deep hole. The baby boy had cried himself to sleep, so Patton just folded the blanket over the boy, then placed him on top of his mother. He buried him alive."

The bodies of Nelly Phillips and Harold Patton were never found. They remain buried somewhere on the Patton farm.

Strangely, some in Henderson County continued to believe that Jess Sweeten beat the confession out of George Patton. But when a reporter questioned George after the trial in Waxahachie, he said, "No, Jess never laid a hand on me. He just questioned me to death."

Be strong!
We are not here to play, to dream, to drift;
We have work to do, and loads to lift;
Shun not the struggle—face it; 'tis God's gift.

Be strong!
Say not, "The days are evil. Who's to Blame?"
And fold the hands and acquiese—Oh Shame!
Stand up, speak out, and bravely, in God's name.

Be strong!
It matters not how deep intrenched the wrong,
How hard the battle goes, the day how long;
Faint not—Fight on! Tomorrow comes the song

Maltbie Davenport Babock

THE WILD MAN OF BAXTER TAPP

Jess and his dog

The legend of a wild man roaming the small community of Baxter Tapp had been told for a period of four years, first by a hunter who claimed to have "shined it's eyes" with a carbide lamp while hunting squirrel south of the old Hume Place. And with each telling, the wild man grew in stature. When a crowd gathered around the pot-bellied stove at the general store, the hunter would began the story.

"Nig was the best grey-eyed Catahoula dog in the country," said the hunter.

'He was trained for coon and possum, but we was hunting squirrel in the bottoms south of the Old Hume place when he got a good sniff of Ol' Joe in the clearing—he lit out of there like a turpentined cat. And the last time I seen that dog he disappeared over the backbone of a ridge—leaving me to fend primarily fer myself! It was a foggy night and that dog was blowing hard enough to run a gin whistle. Now, I'm ashamed to tell it, but my heart was skippin' more beats than a one-arm drummer!

'Measurin' from head to toe," the hunter continued, "that thang spanned a distance of eight feet. And his gross weight was near eighty-five pounds to the runnin' foot. And its head was circumference of a steerin' wheel on a Wichita Log Hauler."

Ol' Joe preferred his meat raw. And for some reason the bones were always found in the fireplace of the old abandoned Hume farm house near Baxter Tapp. Mr. Hume had died several years earlier, and apparently his heirs had left the old farm to rot.

But not knowing the legend, a family of squatters moved in a year or two later, and found a huge pile of bones which had been thrown in the fireplace. They took good care of the farm until Ol' Joe made a return visit one night around midnight—leaving a pile of dirty laundry, several tubs of cooking lard, a good pair of men's work shoes, and a few cooking utensils.

After hearing the story second-hand at the general store, Shack Patterson bragged that he owned four hounds that would whip anything with fang, tooth or claw. And before he realized what he was saying, he had himself a hunting party all liquored-up and headed toward the old Hume place.

Eight men took it upon themselves to rid Baxter Tapp of this legendary wild man. Three carloads of vigilantes followed Shack's truck, and all were toting heavy artillery.

They circled the house several times to flatten the high weeds before coming to a stop in the backyard near the fence. They released the dogs as the bottom part of the sun had touched the tree tops, and it was near dark before they could all agree on a battle plan.

"It's quite possible," said one of the liquored up vigilantes, "that Ol' Joe is stoved-up inside the house." They figured the best thing to do was find some long sticks and beat them against the side of the house. The noise would scare Ol' Joe, and he'd come a running out the back door where they could get a clear shot.

When that plan failed, all agreed that instead of going inside to a certain gruesome death, they'd fan out in a long firing line and shoot up the house.

They fired more than two hundred rounds of various types of ammunition, then re-loaded and fired again. When the smoke cleared, Shack Patterson cautiously led his men inside to search for the carcass.

They carefully searched all five rooms before learning that Ol' Joe had escaped. But evidence was found in the fireplace which proved he had been there, because they found a pile of bloody bones stacked in a neat pile.

By this time the sun had sunk way too low for a proper search of the backwoods. The Hume farm was located near an area of the county that was heavily wooded, and there were a lot of snakes.

So the legend grew. Ol' Joe was indeed a big hairy monster with glowing red eyes. And with this fact selflessly provided by Shack's raiders, they had, more-than-likely, saved the lives of many Baxter Tapp school children.

A month later, a farmer's wife swore she saw Ol' Joe dancing on top of a distant bridge railing. It was under the light of a full moon and she had been washing the supper dishes at the time.

She only got a glimpse, but she was dead certain that what she had seen with her own two eyes was none other than Ol' Joe. "And he was necked as a jay bird!"

Ol' Joe would disappear for months, then reappear seemingly out of thin air. Farmers could tell when he had returned because they would wake up to a gruesome scene in the yard or pen.

Some would find half eaten chickens laying in the coop, others would find dead hogs with only the hams missing. If an animal had been the culprit, the carcass would be torn to pieces. Sheriff Sweeten was summoned.

Jess followed a trail of blood until it disappeared in the thick underbrush. A plaster cast was made of several large, bare footprints near a sandy area at the farmer's back fence. They appeared to be made by a human, and the weight was guessed at two hundred pounds.

But, if Ol' Joe was human, why was he eating raw meat?

Jess had another mystery on his hands.

Sweeten formed a proper search party of heavily-armed deputies who had heard all the hair-raising stories before. He used his own dogs, two bloodhounds. A bloodhound will stay a trail better than any known dog, and will literally run themselves to death before giving up. If unsuccessful, they will not eat for days afterward.

Dallas Cramer, Elton Corley and Homer Williams would aid in the search. The plan called for Jess to start at the hog pen with Bonnie and Clyde where they could pick up the scent. They would trail Ol' Joe to the Hume place, since that seemed to be where he always ended up.

Homer, Elton and Dallas were to park their cars on the road, then walk the half mile distance to the house. They were to hide inside the Hume farmhouse and wait until Ol' Joe arrived.

Ol' Joe seemed to always end up at the farm, so Jess figured the dogs would scare him enough to seek safety there and the deputies could then take him into custody.

Dallas volunteered each deputy to remain all night if it became necessary —but he sure hoped it would not be so.

Homer looked slightly worried, but bravely said that, if the other two would stay, then he'd do the same. And if Ol' Joe came creeping around, he would gladly blister his butt with a load of .00 buckshot.

It was dusk by the time they arrived at the old farmhouse and all three hunkered down for a long wait. They could hear the distant howling of Bonnie and Clyde somewhere deep in the snake-infested bottoms. They were hot on a trail, and seemed to be headed toward the Hume farm. Homer peeked through a broken window pane.

"It sure is dark out there. I can't see a thing."

"Yeah!" said Cramer, "But keep your voice down." Homer continued looking toward the back pasture. Dallas stood watch near the front door. Now he hear the faint cries of a whippoorwill—the barking had stopped. The hairs on Homer's neck stood on end.

"Hell, if you lit a match, you'd have to light two more to see if the first one was burning."

Dallas noticed that Homer and Elton had begun to twitch with each sound. He laughed softly, chastising both.

"Boys, don't worry about the night sounds," he said with a nervous laugh. "The time to worry is when they stop."

Homer laughed nervously. "Well if I see two big red eyes coming toward me, this old house is gonna' have a new back door!"

It had been two hours since they last heard the dogs bark. They had begun to squirm with leg cramps when suddenly Homer's keen ear picked up the faint sound of rustling weeds on the north side of the house. It was coming toward them alright—making heavy steps and just creeping along. It was the kind of steps Ol' Joe would make.

Homer's heart began to race with each step slowly making its way toward the front porch. He heard a plank squeak. Then another. It was a heavy squeak, then the screen door slowly opened. Ol' Joe was coming home to roost. Homer could hear his own heart beating. So could Elton Corley. They aimed their shotguns toward the front door as the knob slowly turned.

"Boo!" yelled Jess, then quickly opened door.

"Damn!" Homer yelled. "Is that you Jess?"

Jess entered laughing.

Homer shined his spotlight toward the front door and noticed that Jess had a man in hand-cuffs. He had captured The Wild Man.

"I'd like you to meet Ol' Joe." said Jess. "He was hiding in the bushes about three miles from farmer's house.

Ol' Joe, as it turned out, was an escapee from the asylum at Terrell, Texas. He was a very pleasant and half naked, forty-five year old man with a long beard and filthy long hair. A strange hollow-eyed man who, for some reason, returned like a homing pigeon to Baxter Tapp.

When Jess asked the man why he ate raw meat, the man told a very sad tale. One that brought tears to the lawmen " When I was a boy," he said, "I played with some matches and it burned our house down. My daddy said if I ever done it again, he'd have me put away. Well, later I guess did it again, and it accidentally set the barn afire.

Then he took me up to Terrell and made me stay in that real bad place. I promised I'd be good if he'd just give me one more chance. That's all I wanted, just one more chance to prove that I'd never start another fire in my whole life. I promised God I'd never ever do it again either if he'd tell that to Daddy—but I guess he didn't hear me. So Daddy just left me there."

"Did your daddy come to visit you?" Jess asked.

"No, I never saw him again anymore."

"How old were you when your daddy left you there?"

"I was twelve."

"Why do you always come here?"

"This is Mr. Hume's house! And when I was fourteen, I escaped out of Terrell to try and find my Daddy, but he had done moved. Then I met Mr. Hume and he told me that I was always welcome at his house. I always come to visit him but he ain't never home. I love Mr. Hume. He's the best friend I've ever had in the whole world.

"So you ate the meat raw rather than build a fire?"

"Yes, because if you promise God, then you're supposed to be real serious about that."

"Did you ever think that eating raw meat could make you sick?"

"Not if you ask Jesus to bless it for you. Mr. Hume said no food would make you sick if Jesus blessed it. Jesus is even better than Mr. Hume. And someday, he's going to help me find my Daddy!"

Next morning, Jess bought a new pair of Levis and a cotton shirt for the Wild Man. Then afterward, took him to the barber shop and had the barber give him a shave and haircut. Several bystanders looked on in amazement—because now "Ol' Joe The Wild Man" looked as normal as any man in town.

Dr. Henderson examined Ol' Joe and pronounced that his mental capacity was about the same as a ten year-old child. They had no choice but to return the Wild Man to the asylum at Terrell, Texas.

Six months later, Ol' Joe escaped for the last time; apparently to find his Daddy. He was never heard from again—.

The fastest gun alive

*Subject has plenty of faith with a potato
But not with a cigarette*

Hazel shows how it's done

Jess Sweeten and Daughter Jessie Nell

Friend and assistant Gus Sours helping Jess with a shooting Demonstration

Sweeten shoots for 10,000 Boy Scouts in Los Angeles, California

Famous Ranger
Captain, Manuel T. (Lone Wolf) Gonzuallas

A Full Arsenal

THE GERMAN MURDER CASE

"Sheriff—Mr. and Mrs. German is dead! There was an awful fire. We can see their bodies in the house—"

Sheriff Sweeten banged down the receiver, cutting off the babbling, hysterical voice, and reached for his coat and hat. His face was grim with the shock of what he had just heard. William Turner German and his wife were an aged couple who'd resided in the Stoddard community near Athens for forty years. Everyone knew them loved them.

When he drove into the German farmyard, he stared grimly at the smoldering, reeking ruins that had once been the almost luxurious home. A group of neighbors stood about the charred remains, talking in low tones. A farmer hurried forward, said, "Sheriff, walk over to the other side. You can see the bodies over there."

Jess complied. An exclamation escaped him. Visible in the smoking debris were two charred objects that were almost unrecognizable as human bodies. The smaller body lay on the twisted wreckage of a small cot, arms twisted grotesquely. The second was huddled on the floor, several feet away.

Jess glanced toward the crowd. "Anyone have an idea what happened?" He kept his voice steady with a visible effort.

A middle-aged farmer stepped forward. "I got here first, I guess. I live right across that field there. When I saw the fire I called the neighbors and then hurried over to see if Mr. and Mrs. German were alright. I couldn't find them. The whole place was already going up in smoke."

"Their gasoline stove must have exploded," said another. "They used one of those old-fashioned hand pump-kinds."

Sweeten's keen glance was going over the debris. His eyes fell on a five-gallon gasoline can, exploded and battered out of shape. From one rim trailed a wire which had obviously served as a bale.

"What time did the Germans usually retire?"

"Sometimes pretty early," a neighbor volunteered. "Both of them were pretty old, you know, and not in very good health."

Without further comment the sheriff turned back toward the house. "We should be able to get in there to dig around pretty soon," he commented in a low voice to deputy Elton Corley. "Get this crowd out of here and let's see what we can find."

Deputy Corley glanced at him. "Jess, do you think it wasn't an accident?"

"I don't know, Elton. The Germans have lived in this house for nearly forty years, and they've been using gasoline for a long time. I don't think they'd have likely been careless with it."

As the officers were clearing the yard, a slender, visibly excited Negro came running down the pathway. He was gasping for breath as if he had hurried a long distance. Sweeten recognized him as Huey Fulton, who had been the Germans handyman for years.

"It ain't true is it?" Huey gasped, as he neared the sheriff. "A man said Mr. and Mrs. German got burned up! That ain't true, is it?"

Sweeten regarded him thoughtfully. "I'm afraid it is, Huey. Where have you been? Do you sleep here?"

"No, sir. I just work here days. Nights I go home to Athens. I left here tonight at six." The Negro was staring fixedly at the ashes, his eyes distended with horror. He bent foreword slightly and a strange, forlorn wail came from his lips. "Poor old folks—they been like my own folks for ten years, them German's have...."

"Huey, look," Sweeten pointed. See that gasoline can over there in the ashes? Did Mr. German keep it in his room?"

The Negro crept closer. "Mista' Jess," he said, presently, "that ain't our can."

"Are you sure?"

"It was part of my job to look out for gas and kindlin'. I knows every can on 'dis place. Come here. Look, I'll shows 'ye." He led the way to the out-building and opened the door. Leaning over, he groped in the gloomy interior, and came up with a can in his hands. It was bright and clean, and half filled with gasoline. "This here's our can. I never seen that other'n before."

Sweeten turned thoughtfully away. He hastened the last of the loitering spectators on their way and then went back in the smoldering ruins.

"Well, let's see what we can find," he said, "that gasoline can interests me."

They worked gingerly for a while in silence. Suddenly the sheriff exclaimed, "It was no accident Elton. Look here!" He walked away from the smoke, and held out a ruined object. "This was lying beneath the old man."

The deputy stared. "A gun!"

"Yeah, Lying right beneath him, as if he had dropped it. Another thing, neither one of those bodies is anywhere near that gasoline can. And you'll notice that the lamp is not exploded. Mrs. German is on the cot—but the old man is very near the door. When people have lived in the same house for forty years, they'd have to be pretty badly confused, even injured, not to be able instinctively to find their way out. If one had been hurt and the other trapped when he went back to help, the bodies would be close together. But look at them."

Fulton was standing nearby, muttering under his breath. "Mr. German ever have trouble with any of his neighbors?" Sweeten asked.

"I don't reckin' so. I never heard him say nothing about it." He added darkly, "but they's a lot of sneak thieves around here. And Mrs. German, she always feedin' some tramp. Mr. German, he kept warnin' her. Some day, he say, she gonter wish she tol' 'em to go on about their business."

When the sheriff examined the pistol, he made a discovery that appeared to bolster his ugly suspicion. Five shells were in the chamber and all had been discharged. "Four by the intense heat—" he pointed out, "—but the fifth was discharged by the hammer. You can see the dent made by the firing pin." He stared into space, his eyes very speculative.

Could someone have knocked at the door, maybe someone the old man feared or mistrusted, so that he went back for his gun?"

By the time the coroner's inquest was complete, it was obvious that Sweeten had foul murder on his hands. Ugly holes in Mrs. German's skull indicated that she had been beaten to death. A .22 rifle shot was lodged inside the old man's cranium!

When the ghastly news became known, the community was in an uproar. Rumors flew thick and fast, and hundreds of tips began to pour in. On the date of the crime—September 25, 1934—two hoboes had stopped at several farm houses in the area. In one instance, one of those men had made insulting advances to a housewife. He had also demanded money.

Automatically the sheriff turned to a rigorous check of Huey Fulton, the Germans, handyman. He had a clear-cut alibi, substantiated by several relatives and friends. Neighbors of the murdered couple testified that he was of good character and had steady work habits.

He followed the officers about. "I'm gonter help you git the man that kilt Mr. and Mrs. German."

In the evening, while the officers were at the German farm, a deputy called for Sweeten's attention. "Jess, come have a look at these tracks."

Faintly outlined in the rocky backyard, and leading away by a circuitous route toward the front gate, were footprints. "Look at the design of the heels. These marks are steel heel-plates. And see, on the left one, the plate is loose and slews off to one side. It's that way on all of the left tracks." Excitedly they followed the prints, only to be disappointed when they disappeared abruptly on the hard surfaced highway.

Sweeten turned the facts over in his mind. The motive could possibly be robbery. Neighbors had said that the old man had recently displayed several hundred dollars he had gotten from the sale of some property. A check at his bank revealed that he had made no deposit since August 1st.

There were other possibilities. Revenge. In the course of his forty years in Stoddard community, had Turner German made an enemy who nursed a grudge, and had silently awaited a chance for retaliation? Both Turner and his wife had been kind and generous people, the soul of honesty, but the shrewd sheriff had long since learned that a twisted, warped mind could bear a murderous grudge against the most innocent of persons.

Early the following morning, Huey Fulton rushed into Sweeten's office. He was visibly perturbed. "I think I've found somethin'! You know those tracks we saw in the yard? Well, I've found some more of them, almost a mile away from the house!"

Summoning Deputy Elton Corley, Sweeten hurried at once with Huey to the scene. There the Negro pointed out his discovery. In a piece of plowed ground, near a thick clump of timber, were tracks identical to the ones which had led out of the German yard. The three followed the tracks for a distance. Sometimes with difficulty where they were obliterated in the hard earth, later they would pick them up again.

Suddenly Sweeten tensed, "Listen..." He began to run forward. The others followed. From somewhere nearby, there was the sound of a running motor. They burst into a clearing and paused in surprise. A dilapidated old Chrystler coupe sat in the edge of the timber—motor humming. The doors sagged open. There was no one in sight. Quickly, the officers strode forward.

Sweeten exclaimed, "There's some more of those tracks, leading out of that car! The killer had his car hidden out here, and didn't dare come back for it until today. He must have been ready to make his getaway and heard us coming!" He plunged toward the trees. "Come on—he can't be far ahead!"

It became obvious within a few moments that whoever left the car had gained a head start sufficient to insure his escape. Sweeten ordered his deputy to the nearest telephone to summon reinforcements, and dogs to trail the fugitive.

Then Jess returned to the abandoned automobile, cut the switch, and made a careful scrutiny of the interior. It was bare of any objects save for a large pocket knife hidden in a slit of upholstery. Deftly sliding a handkerchief beneath it to avoid obliterating possible fingerprints. Sweeten lifted the knife.

Fulton leaned foreword. "That's Mr. German's knife," he said.

"Are you sure?"

"Yes, sir. I scaled fish with that knife, many times. Mr. German, his son, gave it to him as a present." Huey walked around the car, inspecting it. "That car don't belong to nobody around here," he said positively. "Ain't nobody around here got that kind." He stared at the crumpled fenders, the weather-worn paint and battered body, and added with a tinge of scorn, "That's po' folks car!"

The sheriff leaned foreword. "Huey, listen...sometimes people get sore at a man over a little thing, something that doesn't even seem important at the time. But they keep it on their minds, and—"

Fulton broke in. "I know what you say, but Mr. German, he never had no trouble with nobody! I knowed him ten years."

Dogs were brought, and a posse hastily organized to scour the vicinity for the fugitive, but he had successfully eluded them. Sheriff Sweeten took another tack. He advertised widely for the origin of the Chrysler, and with almost immediate results. From a Dallas company came word that it had been purchased there several days previously, by a C. S Johnson. Another investigation showed that the man had given a phony name and non-existant Athens address. He had paid cash for the car.

"This Johnson," the sales manager informed Sweeten, "Was a colored man. A great big fellow—about thirty-five or forty. "He added some pertinent details. "He was a round-shouldered, soft spoken man...Wait a minute! I remember something else, Sheriff. When the fellow signed the papers I noticed that he had scars on both hands."

"What kind of scars?"

"Well, I remember a fellow that was born with six fingers on one hand. The fellow had it removed, but it left a scar just like the Negro's scar. Except the Negro had scars on both hands."

Back in Athens, Sweeten appealed to Huey Fulton, repeating the car salesman's description of "Johnson." Fulton reflected for a long while. "Lots of colored folk in Athens look like that," he muttered. "But them scars—no, sir. Don't reckin I ever seen anybody that once had his self six fingers."

For several days the search for the mysterious Johnson and the effort to establish his true identity went forward, without success. Within his own mind, Sweeten was sure "Johnson" was the killer who had brutally clubbed and shot Mr. and Mrs. Turner German, before setting fire to the house.

All efforts to link him with the couple failed, however, since they had never employed help prior to the time they engaged Huey Fulton.

Fulton told Sweeten, ruefully, "I been lookin' at folks' hands until I'm blind in the eyes, but I ain't seen no scars where they's been fingers cut off."

In a despairing effort to re-construct the whole thing in his mind Sweeten returned to the German farm and spent the better part of the day tramping about the place, studying the setting.

In a corn field, not far from the house, he came upon a new set of odd tracks believed to be the killer's. Suddenly he stopped, staring at the ground. A second set of tracks approached—from the direction of the German house. They were narrower than the first prints, and differed in other respects. The two sets met, and the scuffed ground at that point indicating that two men had stood there together for some short time, probably conversing. Then both turned and proceeded together in the direction the suspect had originally been traveling!

For a long time, Jess kneeled motionless beside the tracks. At length he whistled softly beneath his breath. "*Well, what do you know about that*!"

Thereafter, for several hours, Jess was extremely busy. Returning to his car for paraphernalia, he made trips to the clearing where the roadster had been found, to the yard, and back to the corn field, making plaster casts of various prints. Then he drove hurriedly to town. He talked with several persons in the colored section, then drove to the home of Mrs. A. G. Pruitt. "Where's your son Elmer?" he asked.

"I couldn't rightly say," she answered. "He's off lookin' for work. You suspicious he done something bad?"

"I don't know yet, Mrs. Pruitt, but there are some questions I'd like to ask him. By the way, does he have a car?"

"Yes, sir. He got one right lately as a matter of fact, but I don't know where it is."

"Does he have a gun of some sort?"

"Yes, sir. It's some kind of a rifle."

"You reckon it might be a twenty-two?"

"Might, but I don't know anything about them things."

In looking about the shabby home, he found a pair of soiled khaki trowsers, unmistakably splattered with blood. Some of the spots had been rubbed with soil, in an apparent attempt to disguise the stains. Jess turned with the trowsers in his hands and as he was leaving, he added casually, "Elmer was born with six fingers on each hand, wasn't he?"

Sensing trouble for her boy, she was near tears. "Yes, sir, but I took him to the doctor and had 'em operated."

Back in his office, Sweeten told his deputies, "I want Elmer Pruitt. Send his description to every newspaper and sheriffs office and police department in the country. Tell 'em he's wanted for the murder of Mr. and Mrs. German!" As they stared at him, startled, he calmly exploded his bombshell. "And after we catch up with Pruitt, we'll nab the guy that engineered the whole thing. Huey Fulton!"

Their mouths fell open. "But Fulton was in the clear!"

"We thought he was. He fooled me, too. That guy should have been an actor—"

"How did you get on to him?"

"Those footprints," Jess said. I found a batch of them out in the corn field, where our killer met someone, stood and talked to him, and then they went off together Naturally, I'd already taken a look at Fulton's footprints plenty, to be sure they didn't match those first ones we found. Of course they didn't, but they matched the prints of the guy who met the killer out in the corn field. We thought all along it might

159

be someone who knew a lot about the Germans. Well, Fulton gave the inside dope to Pruitt. The minute I knew those were his prints, it was easy to figure out who might have been with him. His closest friend is this Pruitt. In fact, they're kin by marriage.

"It had to be someone Fulton trusted and was mighty friendly with. They had it figured out to the minute, all right. Only it was dumb of Huey to lead us to the car and the other prints, and forget that, not far away he left his own footprints with those of the killer. That's why Huey couldn't remember anyone around Athens who had scarred hands; he didn't want to remember. That's why he kept steering us toward a tramp, to throw us off the scent. With his good reputation, his air-tight alibi and his eagerness to help us, his plan was foolproof...almost.

"Aren't you going to arrest him?"

"Not now. He thinks he's safe and he's enjoying his role in the limelight. He won't go anywhere, and if we don't put the finger on him, he may lead us to Pruitt. He may even believe he can keep Pruitt from talking, if we catch him. Well, now we want Pruitt."

Once it became known that the authorities were searching for Elmer Pruitt as the suspect in the German murder, dozens of tips came flooding in.

An Athens Negro revealed that at about midnight, the night of the killing, Pruitt had paid him five dollars to drive him to Dallas, about eighty miles away. Pruitt had said his own car was "some place where I can't get at it."

A Dallas man, proprietor of an undertaking establishment, and a former Athens resident, volunteered the information that Pruitt was staying in Dallas. "He showed me a slip that he had two-hundred dollars on deposit with the desk clerk."

The authorities sped at once to the Dallas rooming house, only to discover that Pruitt had gone.

Grimly, the search went foreword, concentrating in Van Zandt and Henderson Counties. On October 5th, the fugitive appeared at a farmhouse near Martin Mills, in Van Zandt, and begged food. He was dishevelled and filthy, and had obviously been hiding out in the swamp. He disappeared again before the frightened farm wife could contact the authorities.

Shortly afterward, the elusive killer began a reign of terror among the colored people in various localities, threatening and bullying them into sheltering him. He was wary and shrewd, however, and always managed to keep one jump ahead of the police. From state to state he traveled in a zig zag course, and for ten months the chase went on. Weary and discouraged, yet stubbornly confident of ultimate success, Sheriff Sweeten traveled thirty-thousand miles covering twenty-three states at his own expense, doggedly pursuing Pruitt.

A careful watch set over Fulton revealed nothing, and it was obvious that he knew nothing of Pruitt's whereabouts. He went blithely about his affairs, totally unaware that he was under suspicion, still keeping up his role of "avenging" spirit and loud in his declarations that he wanted the killer caught.

On November 29th, the county was electrified by the news that Pruitt had been captured in Rankin, West Texas. A prisoner being held there answered Pruitt's description perfectly, to the scars where the sixth fingers had been removed, although he vehemently denied that he was Pruitt, or that he had ever been to Athens.

Sweeten made a flying trip to Rankin, to be greeted with new disappointment. The similarity was merely that and nothing more. The prisoner was not Elmer Pruitt!

Thereafter, nothing was heard of the fugitive. He seemed to have disappeared into thin air. At length Sweeten said, "There's always the possibility that he'll try to get in touch with some of his relatives when he thinks the heat is off. His mother thinks he might go to the home of an uncle in Dallas. I'd suggest that we lay low and give him a chance to come in."

Accordingly, a colored man was set to watch the home of Pruitt's uncle, day and night. For eight months the weary schedule was maintained, with no sign of the fugitive. Then on March 4th, 1936, the Negro watcher burst into a Dallas precinct station, wildly excited.

"That man—" he shouted, "—the one you wanted me to watch out for, he's come to roost. He jest' walked right in!"

The officers rushed at once to the scene, and found Elmer Pruitt there, lying on a bed in his uncle's house. He offered no resistance at all, and coolly and promptly admitted his guilt.

"You got me—ain't no use in me to deny it."

Back in Athens, he gave a cold-bloodied recital of the crime, admitting that the officers' suspicions concerning Huey Fulton had been correct. He had gone to the German home about five, meeting Fulton in the corn field. Then he had hidden nearby until about ten-thirty, leaving his car in the clearing. At ten-thirty he had gone to the house, knocked, and asked the old man to change a ten dollar bill.

"I guess he was suspicious of me, because he told me to leave, and he went and got his gun. I shot him once. The woman started screamin'. I had a hammer in my overalls. I beat her over the head with it. She never did get off the bed when I shot him. I guess she was too scared to move."

After ransacking the house and taking the money, Pruitt said he'd poured gasoline out of the drum he had brought with him and had fired the house.

"Then we beat it."

"We—" interrupted Sweeten. "There was someone with you?"

Pruitt looked disgusted at his slip. "I reckon I might as well tell you. Artie Cook—that's a friend of Huey's and mine—he was with me. I got scary about doin' it alone, so I took Artie. I promised him part of the money, only there wasn't as much as Huey said there'd be. It was all Huey's idea. He come and said that the old man had a lot of money, and for me to get it, and we'd divide it up. He said he'd have a real good alibi, and they wouldn't ever know who done it. Anyhow. After we set the house on fire, we started back to the car, only we heard some folks coming across the field and we couldn't go to the car. I went back to get it a few days later, but there was some laws—"

Two deputies slipped from the room to arrest Huey Fulton and Artie Cook. Jess was not particularly surprised at ther evelation concerning Artie Cook. He was a boastful, troublesome Negro whose reputation was none too good.

Pruitt muttered glumly, "That Huey ain't worth nothin'. He acts mighty big, but he's all the time thinkin' up stuff, only he won't do his own dirty work. That's why folks think she's so much. I'd have done better not to listen to him.

Sweeten regarded him contemptuously. "You certainly would," he retorted. "A darn sight better!"

Although taken by complete surprise, Fulton maintained a front of injured dignity. Both he and Cook vehemently denied any part in the crime, but a jury believed differently. June 26, 1936, they returned guilty verdicts against the trio. Pruitt was promptly sentenced to death in the electric chair, Fulton and Cook to life imprisonment.

An appeal failed. On Friday April 30, 1937, Pruitt paid with his life for the atrocious crime. Already, Cook and Fulton—the clever hired hand who was too clever for his own good—had entered the Texas State Prison to serve the rest of their natural lives.

In Athens, citizens and officers felt only grief that the punishment of the trio could not bring back the lives sacrificed at the murderous hands of the man they befriended.

Elmer Pruitt

Hazel and Jess At the Farm

ACCIDENTAL MURDER?

September 17, 1937

The eighty-acre lake near the power plant at Trinidad generated electricity for much of East Texas. The water was crystal clear and well stocked with large bass. The lake was open to the public for fishing, which was a good thing for the company to do in the hard times of the thirties. A bridge was built atop the skimmer-wall with a three-foot handrail. The bridge spanned the entire width of the small lake, and few outside Henderson County knew it's location.

Johnny Beckham learned about the lake from his wife's two brothers who lived in Athens. Although Johnny was only twenty-nine years old, he owned a profitable wholesale poultry business on South Moore street in Tyler, Texas. When his wife Guydel, wanted to visit her mother, Johnny would pick up her two brothers, Billie and Arlton. Together, they would drive to Lake Trinidad for a few hours fishing.

Johnny and Guydel had been arguing for three of the last eight months. His complaint was that she spent money as fast as he could make it. Her argument was that she deserved a better life than she had known before. She was a very attractive woman, easily catching the eye of other men whenever they went out for entertainment.

Guydel loved sporting a never-ending supply of new dresses, jewelry and hats when the business was good, but complained bitterly when it was bad. Johnny, on the other hand, was still in love with his first wife who had died in 1935. He often compared Guydel unfavorably to her, and that was the source of their love-hate relationship.

After the worst sales week of the year, Guydel insisted that he drive her to Athens to visit her mother—he and her brothers should go to the lake and relax. Johnny readily agreed. Anything to get away from the constant nagging. His last nerve was hanging by a thread, and she was playing it like a guitar string. Maybe another trip would ease his worries.

Sunday, September 15, 1937, Guydel filled a picnic basket with sandwiches. At three-thirty they headed toward Athens, which was about thirty-five miles away. When they arrived in Chandler, which is about nine miles from Tyler, Guydel decided to purchase a pint of whiskey from a well known bootlegger.

"This will help you relax," she said. "But you have to promise me that you won't drink any of it until you get to the lake!"

Within half an hour they pulled into the front yard of Mrs. Guy Jackson's home. Johnny waited in the car because he couldn't stand to breath the same air as that old woman.

"Just tell Arlton and Billie to hurry up," he said.

Guydel and her mother were cut from the same cloth. She was a nosy Ol' busybody, and from all appearances both had been weaned on pickles. The last thing Johnny wanted was to waste any of his precious time with her.

"Tell them to hurry up!"

"You could at least come inside and say hello to momma!" Guydel pleaded.

"Hell, no! I've said all I want to say to that old woman!"

Billie was in the backyard chopping sawmill slab for the cook-stove when Guydel ordered him to drop what he was doing. He was told find Arlton and accompany Johnny to the lake. Arlton was visiting the next-door neighbor.

"I bought Johnny a bottle of whiskey," she told Billie, "and you better not drink a drop of it!" she ordered, "It's to calm his nerves. And make sure that Arlton doesn't drink any."

At the lake Johnny parked the car near the bank; baited a hook, then walked thirty feet out on the skimmer-wall bridge and set the cork for six feet. He leaned over the railing then and took a long thirsty sip of whiskey.

Arlton found a suitable spot farther out on the bridge, but not far from Johnny. Complaining that the water was too deep where they were fishing—Billie moved almost to the opposite side of the lake. It was estimated to be somewhere around twelve feet at that point.

Suddenly, and without warning, Johnny Beckham began cursing at the top of his voice. He rushed toward Arlton in a fit of rage—grabbed him around the waist and tried unsuccessfully to throw him in the water.

"You and that dammed whore!" Johnny yelled. "You're all in this together!"

"What's wrong, Johnny?" Arlton shouted in a panicky voice, locking both arms and legs around a support post.

Johnny began kicking Arlton in his ribs while holding his stomach. "You know dammed well what's wrong!" Johnny yelled.

Billie heard the yelling and ran across the bridge and hid behind a stand of broom-weed. He knew Johnny kept a hunting rifle in the trunk of his car. Knowing that his brother-in-law kept a hunting rifle in his car, Billie figured it was best to put as much distance between himself and Johnny as he could.

Arlton released his death-grip on the bridge post after Johnny Beckham fell backward holding his stomach. Cautiously, he eased to Johnny's side; leaned directly over him—but all the while kept a firm grip on the railing with his right hand.

"What's the matter, Johnny?" Arlton cried. "Are you sick?" Arlton noticed his brother Billie peeking from the weeds on the opposite side of the lake. He shouted for help at the top of his voice. "Billie!-"

Arlton's last word would haunt Billie Jackson for the rest of his life because at that very moment he yelled Billie's name, Johnny Beckham lunged foreword, grabbed Arlton around both legs, and pulled him off the bridge. Both men quickly sank to the bottom.

Billie arrived at the scene in time to see Arlton's head and thrashing arms appear only once. Arlton's eyes seemed frozen in a dreadful stare of absolute terror as he sank for the last time. And for a full minute and a half the last breath of Arlton Jackson and Johnny Beckham trickled to the surface in small bubbles.

The double drowning took place at six-thirty in the afternoon, but Billie Jackson waited another two hours before summoning an employee at the power company.

The employee in turn summoned the plant superintendent, Mr. Crews at the local Baptist Church. Mr. Crews quickly reported the incident to Constable Dan Billings in Malakoff. A secretary informed Mr. Crews that Constable Billings was on vacation and could not be reached. Several phone calls later, Mr. Crews reached the Athens Justice of the Peace, B. C. Hall.

By the time Mr. Hall drove to the scene with Deputy Sheriff Elton Corley and the County Coroner, Dr. R. E. Henderson, who would assist him in the inquest, both bodies were laying on the bank near the skimmer-wall bridge.

Asked why he waited two hours to report the accident, Billie told the constable that he had been at the other end of the lake in a boat and had not noticed the accident. He offered that he did report it as soon as he learned both men were missing.

When the bodies were pulled from the lake, Johnny's arms were still locked tightly around the legs of Arlton Jackson. Justice Hall said that this was common in cases of accidental drowning. Apparently one had jumped in to save the other. "A drowning man will often cling to his rescuer," he said, "and this act verifies the fact that this death was accidental."

Johnny Berry testified that, while he was pulling the men to the surface, he had noticed a trickle of blood coming from the nostrils of Johnny Beckham. Justice Hall said that also would prove his theory. "Most likely, the blood was caused from hitting his head during the fall." Again, this was not unusual.

The report read: "Death By Accidental Drowning." The bodies were released to the Burks-Walker-Daniel Funeral home in Tyler, Texas, the home of the late Johnny Beckham. As far as the state was concerned, the case was closed.

The body of Arlton Jackson was returned to Athens for burial, and Johnny Beckham was buried in the Hopewell Cemetery in Tyler.

On her way home from the funeral, Johnny's sister, Hazel Beckham paid a visit to Sheriff Sweeten. Having read many stories about him, she knew that he was a nationally known crime buster. If anyone could learn the real truth about her brother's death, it was Sheriff Jess Sweeten. She did not believe that her brother's death was an accident.

"Sheriff, "I know Johnny's death was ruled as an accident, but I have a gut feeling that he was murdered."

Jess had not personally investigated the accident because the Justice of the Peace had made, what he believed, was a very thorough and professional investigation of the matter. The County Coroner, Dr. Henderson, had been present during the inquest and had agreed that

Johnny's death was as the report stated. "First, Mrs. Beckham. Tell me why you feel that something is amiss."

"Sheriff, for over a month, Johnny had been very troubled over a premonition of his death. So powerful was this premonition that he had his lawyer draw up a last will and testament. He ordered a complete physical check-up from head to toe, and when the doctor pronounced him fit-as-a- fiddle, he went to another doctor and ordered a second opinion.

"I have never seen Johnny so upset. He phoned me at my office in Austin and said, 'Hazel, I think I'm going to die pretty soon, and I just wanted you to know that I've changed my will. Guydel is not going to get a thing. 'He was giving everything he owned to his first wife's sister. He had inherited the oil property from his first wife, and he felt that it was only fair that the property stay with his first wife's family. Johnny's first wife died, but he was still in love with her. He never got over his first wife's death."

"What did you tell Johnny about the premonition?"

"I suggested that the premonition came from the fact that he still missed Linda. And since the premonition came two years after, Linda's death, it was she that he was thinking about."

"Did that calm him down?"

"Yes, somewhat, but it didn't deter him from ordering more life insurance, and paying all his debts a month early."

Jess wrote the information on a note pad and said, "Well, Mrs. Beckham, I'll look into the matter. Where can you be reached?"

"Sheriff, I work for the Commission for the Blind in Austin. You can reach me there."

Jess drove to the County Coroner's office and questioned Dr. Henderson since he was at the scene, and would know whether anything unusual had been noticed on the bodies. The doctor relayed what information the rescuer, Johnny Berry, had said about blood being in Beckham's nostrils. He added that both he and Justice Hall assumed the man had bumped his head on the bridge.

The next person to be questioned by the Sheriff was Johnny Berry, the rescuer. He questioned Berry in detail for a period of two hours. Berry recalled that he indeed had told Justice Hall and the doctor about the bloody nose.

"Mr. Berry, can you remember any other unusual thing about the bodies?"

"Yes, now that you mention it, the body of one of those men seemed as though it had been dead longer than the other body.

"In what way?"

"It was more rigid."

"Which body?"

"The one that was holding the other man's legs. Johnny Beckham."

"Johnny Beckham?"

"Yes, sir, and I don't know whether it's important, but that Beckham fellow also had a little blood in his ears."

"Blood in his ears?"

"Yes, sir, just a trickle in each ear. He had this strange grin on his face"

Jess returned to Athens and questioned the Coroner for the second time.

"Doc, what would cause a man to bleed from his nose and ears?" Jess asked knowingly.

Dr. Henderson's eyes lit up. He nodded, knowing the point that Sweeten had just made.

"Convulsions!"

Johnny Beckham could have suffered convulsions prior to his death. The rigidity of his body seemed to indicate that possibility. Jess now suspected that Johnny Beckham had been poisoned, and the poison used was more-than-likely strychnine.

"Doc, what are the symptoms of strychnine poisoning?"

"Jess, poisoning by strychnine causes a massive series of convulsions. It affects the spinal cord. Within fifteen minutes, the muscles begin to twitch. That's followed by a sensation of suffocation and constriction of the chest. The victim actually dies of exhaustion"

"What does it do to the face?"

"Tetanic Spasm. "

"What's that?"

"The feet and head will bend backward. The face becomes blue and the mouth is contracted in a fixed grin. It's called *risus sardinocus. "*

"Was an autopsy pulled on Johnny Beckham?" Jess asked.

"No," Dr. Henderson replied as if he was angered at himself. "The family didn't request one."

"What member of the family didn't request one?" Jess asked knowingly.

"Guydel, his wife."

Doc Henderson was visibly upset with himself. He like everyone else, assumed that Billie Jackson was telling the truth about the incident. And since Billie was related to both victims, the possibility of him lying about it seemed highly unlikely.

Operating on the theory of foul-play, Jess drove to Tyler and questioned a few of Johnny's neighbors. He wanted to know who Johnny's enemies were and who had motive to kill the man. One neighbor said that Johnny and Guydel's arguments were legendary.

"Guydel was a gold-digger," said another neighbor. "Always putting on airs!"

Another said she spent money like it was like it was a sin to have it. "She was a vulgarian of the highest order," said the neighbor. "Always flaunting the most expensive jewelry in the face of women who couldn't afford such luxuries."

"She liked attention from men other than her husband," said another.

He questioned several of Johnny Beckham's employee's at his poultry Company and learned that Guydel had sold all the remaining chickens for one hundred dollars—a fraction of their actual worth—one day after the funeral. The foreman of Johnny's poultry business said, Guydel boldly walked into the building after the funeral, and fired everybody.

Business associates were questioned. Jess learned that Beckham left a will in a safety deposit box at the Peoples National Bank. He learned that Guydel had sold all the furniture belonging to her late husband. He contacted the man who picked up the trash in that section of Tyler, and was told that he had found many of the family photographs in the trash can.

When Jess questioned the owner of the hardware store, the man said that Johnny walked in about a week before his death and paid his entire bill in cash. "Sheriff, I told Johnny that he was one of my best customers, and it wasn't necessary to pay the whole bill. But he shrugged his shoulders and said, 'here, take it. You might never see me again.'"

Guydel had vacated the house, and her whereabouts was unknown to anyone. A business associate of Johnny Beckham, a man named Watkins, offered another bit of unusual information. He and his wife had been having dinner at the Brown Derby Restaurant on South Broadway when Guydel walked in with a strange man. And what made it even stranger, was the fact that the incident had occurred on the day of the funeral.

Silently and without fanfare, Jess continued his investigation.

After learning about the strange man seen with Guydel, Jess questioned Mrs. Watkins at her home. "The man you and your husband saw with Guydel Beckham at the Brown Derby Mrs. Watkins. What did he look like?"

"Sheriff, he was about five-foot nine or ten, with dark brown hair—"

"Any identifying marks. Tattoos, scars, that sort of thing?"

"Yes, he has three fingers missing on his left hand."

It was time to question Billie Jackson.

At approximately seven o'clock Saturday morning, Jess picked up Billie Jackson and drove to Lake Trinidad. Sweeten told Billie that he had several questions that needed to be resolved before he could close the books on the drowning. Jackson had no idea that Jess was suspicious and was more than happy to offer any assistance the sheriff needed.

Jess followed as Jackson led him out to the spot where both men supposedly fell into the water.

"Sheriff, it's twelve feet deep here," he said, "and I was way down there, in a boat." He pointed to the east end of the lake.

"Did you hear anything? Yelling. That sort of thing?"

"No, sir, I never heard a thing."

"No yelling for help?"

"Well, they might have yelled, but I was too far away to hear anything."

"You didn't hear the water splashing?"

"No, sir."

Jess sought the aid of a power plant employee to help in reconstructing the events of the drowning. He had the man row a boat to the spot where Billie said he had been fishing, then ordered him to stop. He spoke in a normal voice without shouting, and the man stopped the boat.

Jess churned the water with his arm and asked the man if he could hear the splashing water, and the man said that he could hear it plainly. Jess and Billie switched places with the plant employee who repeated the procedure. Both Jess and Billie heard the splashing water.

"Billie," said Jess, "I know that sound travels a lot farther on water than land, and that's what I wanted to show you. If Johnny Beckham or your brother yelled for help, you must have heard him."

"I remember now," Billie said apologetically. "I was in the boat for a while but then I had to take a dump, so I went way out in those high weeds at the end of the lake."

"What time was this?"

"About six-thirty."

"And when you finished taking a dump, where was Johnny and your brother, Arlton?"

"They were gone."

"So, they drown while you were taking a dump in those high weeds?"

"Yes, sir."

"Why did you wait two hours before you went for help?"

"Sheriff, I don't know. I just sat down over there on the bank studying about it. I just couldn't think of what to do."

Jess paused for a long time, then said, "Billie, you saw what happened out here.. And what you saw shocked you pretty good, didn't it?"

There was another long silence. Jess could tell at this point, that Billie Jackson was becoming slightly nervous. Sweeten continued. "That's why you waited two hours before you went for help."

"I just didn't know what to do." Billie mumbled. "I couldn't swim."

"You can't swim?"

"No, sir, not a lick."

"So it wouldn't matter whether you heard them or not would it?"

"No, sir, I guess it wouldn't"

"And there was nothing you could do about it one way or another? You saw it happen, but you were afraid to go out there in that deep water.?"

"Yes, sir."

"So you saw it happen. Right?"

"Yes, sir."

"Now we're getting somewhere. Just tell me exactly what happened. Start from the time when Johnny first picked you and your brother up."

"That Sunday, when Johnny drove to Athens, Guydel told me to take Johnny to the lake. They were arguing a lot that week, so she stopped in Canton and bought Johnny a bottle of whiskey."

"A bottle of whiskey?"

"Yes, sir. It was to calm his nerves."

"So, all three of you were drinking whiskey?"

"No. Just Billie."

"You and Arlton didn't drink any of that whiskey?"

"No, sir!"

"Why not?"

"Guydel told me not to."

Jess wrote the last answer on his note pad.

"Did Johnny drink any of that whiskey before he picked you and Arlton up?"

"No, it was near the lake when he drank the first swig, and then he drank some more after we reached the lake and started fishing from the skimmer-wall."

"Then, what did he do?"

"Well, after we had been fishing thirty minutes, Johnny began to act funny; he looked wild-eyed and began to run and try to catch me and Arlton. He was trying to throw us in the water. Arlton could swim only a little bit and I can't swim at all. So I grabbed hold of a banister post on the bridge with my legs and both hands and held on for dear life. I was trying to keep Johnny from throwing me in the lake. I knew that if he threw me in that deep water I would drown."

"So, he was mad about something. What was he mad about?"

"I don't recall."

"The hell you don't! You were there! You know damn well what he was mad about. What did he say when he was trying to throw you in the water?"

"Well, during the time he was trying to throw us in the water, Johnny said, 'You're all in this together!' You and that whore!—'

"Was he was talking about your sister, Guydel?"

"Yes, I knew he was talking about, Guydel, when he said that. Johnny scuffled harder and longer with Arlton than he did with me. Arlton tried to get Johnny to go on and let him alone and Johnny wouldn't do it. He was cussing every breath, and Arlton managed some way or another to keep Johnny from throwing him in the water at first.

"Finally Johnny laid down on the skimmer wall on his belly and took to groaning something awful, taking on and complaining about his stomach hurting. He looked awful. He lay there for about five minutes.

"Part of the time Arlton was standing over him trying to pick him up. Finally, Johnny roused up and grabbed both of Arlton's feet and legs and pulled him out in the water. They both went off the skimmer wall, Johnny dragging Arlton with him. I went right there and looked at the place where they fell in the water, and in a little bit they came up to the top. I heard and saw Arlton cough one time. But Johnny had a death hold on Arlton.

"In a little bit they sank under the water and I never saw them come up any more until their bodies were dragged out of the water by the rescue party.

"After they went down that last time and didn't come back up I knew they had drowned. I stayed right there on that skimmer wall for a long time, trying to think what to do, and things like that."

"Do you think Guydel poisoned his whiskey?"

"I figured she done something to it."

"When did you suspect that? Before you went to the lake or after you got there?"

"I knew something was wrong. Johnny had gone wild and had a fit because of that whiskey, and in his fit of madness he had pulled Arlton in the water and they drowned."

"When Guydel told you not to drink any of the whiskey, did you suspect that she might have poisoned it?"

"I didn't know what she put in the whiskey, but I knew from what she said that there was something wrong with it."

Jess smiled wide. "And you sure didn't want to drink any of THAT whiskey did you?"

"No, sir!"

"After they drown, you waited two hours. What did you do then?"

"I drove to the gate of the power plant and notified the keeper. And within thirty minutes they pulled them out."

"What did you do with the bottle of whiskey that Johnny had been drinking from?"

"Later that night, I threw it out the window while driving home to Athens."

"Didn't you feel a little uneasy that Arlton might take a drink of the whiskey?"

"While we were going down there I felt uneasy, but I didn't feel uneasy for myself or Arlton because I told him not to drink any of it."

"You told him that while you were at your mother's house in Athens?"

"Yes, sir."

"Because you had a feeling that Johnny wasn't coming back alive. Is that a fair statement?"

"That Sunday when we left Athens to go fishing I felt that Johnny would not come back from the fishing trip alive. But, when Arlton got drowned, it was a great shock to me. I had not thought about Arlton getting killed.

"So, when Johnny started throwing that fit, you figured it was the poison whiskey doing it's work?"

Yes, sir."

Billie Jackson, had lived with Johnny Beckham and his wife Guydel in Tyler from October through February 1936. He said the couple had quarreled a great deal. Guydel had complained that, since she was living with him, Johnny's will should name her as his beneficiary instead of his sister-in- law, who lived in Muskogee, Oklahoma.

In Billie' formal statement which he later signed at the jail, he said that Guydel had told him that she intended to get shed of Johnny some way or another. "On one occasion," Billie confessed, "Guydel asked me if I would go hunting with Johnny and accidentally shoot him, and I told her, 'Hell no, I wouldn't kill anybody!'"

Although Johnny and Guydel had been living together since some time in September 1935, Billie said that Guydel and Johnny were not legally man and wife.

After the confession, Jess drove Billie Jackson to the section of highway where the whiskey bottle was supposedly tossed out the window. Using Billie Jackson and three deputies, Jess searched a five mile stretch of highway from Trinidad to Malakoff; including a portion of the Cedar Creek bottoms, for over four hours. The bottle was not found.

Jackson was returned to the Athens jail where he was charged as a principal instead of an accessory in the crime, since he knew the whiskey had been poisoned before they left Athens. Jess based the arrest on the theory that Billie had aided in taking Johnny Beckham away from any chance of medical assistance.

After the futile search for the whiskey bottle, Jess made another trip to Tyler. This time to present an application for the disinterment of Beckham's body. The following Friday, a hearing before the Justice of the Peace in Tyler was held on the application, and the disinterment order was issued.

Results of the autopsy made by Dr. Henderson, after the disinterment, would take at least six weeks. Jess Sweeten took specimens of the stomach, spleen, kidneys and intestines to the laboratory of the Department of Public Safety in Austin for a chemical analysis to determine whether or not Johnny Beckham's organs contained traces of poison. If Beckham had been poisoned, only strychnine and arsenic would show in the analysis.

Dr. Henderson said that he could not determine whether or not Beckham had been poisoned, but the stomach defiantly showed that Beckham had suffered convulsion, and that was evidence to the fact that he may have been the victim of foul play.

The whereabouts of Mrs. Beckham was still unknown at the time, but reports were received that she had been seen again in Tyler—with the same unknown man.

Jess sent a pick-up order to officers of the adjoining counties, and placed a constant surveillance on the home of Guydel's sister in Corsicana. The questioning of Billie Jackson continued that Friday night. After being allowed to sleep all afternoon, he was brought from his first-floor cell to the living room of Sheriff Sweeten's apartment in the jail at eight o'clock. Jackson brought new evidence into the case as he answered more questions from sheriff Sweeten, Dr. Henderson, and R. T. Craig, a representative of the local newspaper.

"On the day of Johnny's funeral in Tyler, Guydel took me aside and told me not to say anything about what happened." He also admitted that she had promised to "send him some money." He denied a report that he had gone to the Athens post office daily in anticipation of receiving the money from his sister. "She never sent me any," he said.

Jackson stuck to the principal points of his original confession as he again detailed the death of Beckham and his own brother at Trinidad lake. He was questioned for three full hours before being returned to his cell. The sheriff acceded to a request that he not be placed "upstairs" with the other prisoners.

Then, at approximately eight-thirty Saturday morning, Guydel walked into Sheriff Sweeten's office with her attorney Richard Siglar and surrendered. Mrs. Beckham said that she was only awaiting a conference with her two attorneys before surrendering and naturally did not want to come in without conferring with them.

Guydel was wearing an expensive black dress and hat, and was very composed. She smiled at a reporter who was taking her picture, then followed Jess and her attorney, Richard Sigler to the living room of Jess' apartment inside the jail.

Jess immediately began the questioning.

"Mrs. Beckham, I have a few questions concerning portions of your brother's statement."

"You shouldn't hold anything against that boy for what he said in his statement, Sheriff. He was shocked over the tragedy and was in a frantic state of mind."

Guydel sat down next to her attorney, Richard Sigler with an air of confidence. She smiled often at the Sheriff, and seemed to be flirting with her eyes. If that was an attempt to throw Jess off, she had underestimated his ability to see through the facade.

"Mrs. Beckham, what was the condition of your husband's mental health?"

"Sheriff, Johnny had threatened suicide many times. He was given to worry a great deal. He would grieve over the most insignificant matters."

"And his physical health. What condition was that?"

"He had heart trouble and drank heavily. I frequently had to lock up his guns to keep him from taking his own life. Such occasions were numerous in recent months."

"Mrs. Beckham, you know that Billie Jackson in his signed statement had given some very damaging evidence. He told of being warned by you 'not to drink the whiskey that you gave him,' and also to warn Arlton not to do so."

"My goodness, Sheriff, I never said any such thing. If those boys wanted to drink whiskey, I sure couldn't stop them from doing so. Could I?"

"In another place, Mrs. Beckham, Billie said that you asked him to take Johnny hunting and accidentally shoot him. Do you deny that you told him to do that?"

"Jess. May I call you Jess?"

"If you prefer, Mrs. Beckham."

"Jess, sometimes, being flustered, I may have said something like that. Most women do when they're angry, but if I did, Billie knows that I wasn't serious."

"Did you kill your husband, Mrs. Beckham?

"Jess, I loved my husband and he loved me. Of course I did not kill him."

Mrs. Beckham, who was 28 years old and very attractive, did not seem greatly disturbed over the statement that her brother charged against her. She told the reporter who stood nearby "I am not guilty and I am not afraid. I loved Johnny devotedly. I certainly wouldn't want to kill my husband and my own brother."

Recounting her year-and-a-half of life with Beckham, Guydel said Johnny had frequently shown his devotion to her and that he had often, in the presence of others, told her that he loved her better than life itself. She said that she and her husband frequently hunted and fished together and that they were great companions. She quoting a Mr. Hitt of Tyler as saying, "her husband worshipped her."

Guydel admitted that she had removed the furniture from the home occupied by herself and the deceased from Tyler to a house in Corsicana, but she did not know the address or street number. She also admitted selling two-hundred and twenty chickens, receiving a total of one-hundred dollars for them. Other personal effects of the deceased also were disposed of. She admitted to Sweeten that the will drawn up by Johnny Beckham was in her possession, stating that it was at her residence -not at the bank.

Jess stopped the questioning at that point and said,   "Mrs. Beckham, at this time, I'm placing you under arrest for murder."

Guydel smilingly asked a photographer to take a picture of her and the famous lawman before she was placed in a cell. She joked with a number of bystanders as the flashlight bulb flashed in the ante room outside the sheriff's office and seemed to relish the attention of the dozen or so people who were standing by.

At his cell on the ground floor of the county jail, Billie Jackson answered questions poured at him by a half-dozen newspapermen. He also posed for pictures.

A Tyler physician that Saturday morning substantiated the opinion advanced by Dr. Henderson that the blood found on Beckham's body as it was taken from Trinidad Lake came from his ears and mouth following the convulsions believed caused by poisoning.

Attorney, Richard Sigler waived an examining trial for his two clients and agreed to bond of five-thousand dollars for Guydel, and two-thousand-five-hundred dollars for Billie Jackson. Both would appear before the grand jury on September 6th.

Guydel also employed, Earnest Goens, a widely known Tyler attorney, as defense counsel to work with attorney Richard Siglar of Athens. She had already conferred with the Tyler attorney at his office before she turned herself in. Goens was a former State Commander of the American Legion and was well known in East Texas.

The life insurance policy that Johnny ordered, however, was not in effect at the time of his death. He had passed the examination, but there was a waiting period—and he died three days before it would have been in effect.

Six weeks passed before the report came from Austin. To Sweeten's surprise, the report was inconclusive. It stated that the specimens may have contained strychnine but not in sufficient amounts to cause Beckham's death.

This news came as a bomb-shell to the folks of the neighboring counties. Guydel's attorneys had a field day with newspaper reporters gathered around the courthouse in Athens.

"This report from Austin proves my client is innocent!" boasted Richard Siglar.

Guydel relished the attention; and when Jess walked by the crowd on his way to his office, she insisted on having another picture taken with the famous sheriff. Jess knew that she wanted the photograph, not as a memento, but as a trophy to hang on her mantelpiece. It was her way of telling the sheriff that she had won. He stopped and allowed the photographer to snap the picture anyway.

Almost everyone in both counties figured that the long ordeal was over. Jess had been unable to present any physically condemning evidence in the case. All he had was the statement made by Billie Jackson. Siglar and Earnest Goens could easily discredit his statements on the witness stand. Richard smelled victory, so they celebrated with a steak dinner at the Brown Derby Restaurant in Tyler.

But while they were celebrating, Jess Sweeten was not through with Guydel Jackson Beckham. While her and her attorney's partied, he ordered a second disinterment of Beckham's body. This time the entire stomach, spleen, kidneys and intestines were sent to Austin. And to everyone's amazement, Jess Sweeten prevailed on his second attempt. The report came back positive. Johnny Beckham had enough strychnine in his body to kill ten men.

To seal Guydel's fate, Jess learned that a close friend of Guydel Beckham had purchased the poison at a local pharmacy in Tyler. The woman testified that Guydel wanted to poison a neighbor's barking dog. Guydel Jackson Beckham was sentenced to life. Billie received ninety-nine years at Huntsville. The stranger with three missing fingers was not charged.

Time To Retire

THE THREAT TO KIDNAP JESSIE NELL

Jess walked to the post office, opened his box then took out a stack of mail. Among the letters was a penny postcard which read:

Warning; your daughter, Jessie Nell will be kiddnapped between now and November the first. You put me in jail and I'm getting even. You put $1000.00 at the last tree in the graveyard; next to Mrs. Royall's house by Nov. 1st..

Yours Truly;

A Man

P.S. This is a man.

The postmaster had read the postcard before Jess removed it from the box, and alerted the F.B.I. in Dallas. Jess received a call from the bureau within the hour offering their assistance in solving the case, but Jess declined the offer, "I know the criminal element in Henderson County better than anyone, and if I can't solve this case, I don't deserve to be the Sheriff."

Jess carefully read the postcard at his desk and noticed the word "Kidnapped" was misspelled. All the words on the postcard were written without excessive pressure—indicating that the author of the letter may not have been the angry writer. One word appeared to have been written by a second person. All other words were spelled correctly, suggesting that the writer had a formal education. Most criminals did not. The post script reaffirmed the fact that the author was a man. This led Jess to believe that the letter was dictated to a girl, and possibly two girls; since one word was quite different than the other words.

The postcard was mailed from Trinidad. The received-time was stamped at four o'clock in the afternoon. *How would an outsider know the full name of his daughter*? Jess thought to himself.

He called the principal of the local school, and asked that samples of each child's handwriting be made available on the following day. Jess dictated a letter to the principal which contained all the words found in the threat, but in a different way.

The handwriting produced two prime suspects.

He questioned each girl for about ten minutes and both confessed that two men paid them one dollar each to write it. They did not know the name of either man, but they were able to give the Sheriff a pretty good description of the pair.

Jess recognized both men immediately. They worked at the gas station in Trinidad.

He drove to the station and quickly noticed that both men acted nervous about his sudden visit. "I received your damn letter yesterday; so, get in the car and we'll go to the graveyard and settle up."

One looked angrily at the other and said with a whisper, "See, I told you he'd find out about it!"

Jess drove the men to the graveyard, then led them to the large oak tree where he had placed a paper sack of torn newspapers, "There's your damn money; right where you told me to put it. I hope you boys are satisfied. But I'd count it if I were you."

As they nervously leaned over to pick up the sack, Jess knocked them to the ground, then helped them to their feet and knocked them down again. The whipping continued until their heads could pass for mincemeat at the state fair.

Jess ordered them to leave Henderson County or be shot on sight. They quickly left the county.

Judge Ben Dent asked Jess if he intended to file charges against the two, and Jess smiled wryly, "No, I think they've learned their lesson."

SUICIDE, HELL! THAT WAS MURDER

April 24, 1938

Springtime is the very essence of life. It's the time when the farmer plants his crop and the merchant sets his yearly sales quota. Women plan social events and children simply enjoy the promise of a new adventure in the deep east Texas woods.

There was talk of "cotton weather" in the air. And with a little rain, nature promised a very good year for everyone. That promise, however, was broken with a single phone call on a lovely Sunday morning to Sheriff Jess Sweeten.

"Sheriff's office."

"Is this Sheriff Sweeten?"

"Yes, sir. What can I do for you?"

"Sheriff, this is Karl Lambright. You better get down here quick! My grandson just run up to my house and told me that his daddy just shot hisself"

"What's his daddy's name?"

"Walker Lambright. He's my son."

"Where does Walker live?"

"He lives about two miles south of my place. You'll see a big ol' Heart brand fertilizer sign hanging on the fence post. You take a right at that sign. His house is on the left-hand side of the road."

"Where do you live?"

"Down here in Modoc Community!"

"Wait right there, Mr. Lambright. I'm on my way."

Jess informed his deputy, Homer Williams, while rushing toward the door, "Homer, I'm making an emergency run down to Modoc Community. A fellow named Walker Lambright has been shot down there. I don't know how bad he's been hit because his five-year-old boy reported the shooting to his grandpa. I want you to round up the justice of the peace, Dr. Henderson and an ambulance. Get them down there as quick as you can!"

Jess handed Homer the crude map he had scribbled while talking to Karl Lambright, then jumped into the big Buick cruiser and sped out of town.

He drove south for a distance of ten miles before noticing the bright red fertilizer sign hanging on a fence post. Grandpa Lambright was standing near the sign frantically waving his arms. Jess slid to a stop after turning the corner.

Karl Lambright was sobbing as he rushed to the passenger door of the sheriff's car. He quickly stepped inside and said, "Sheriff, Walker's wife Angie just got here with the kids. She told me that Walker was dead; then she collapsed on the bed. My wife called the doctor to come see about her. Mentally, she's in pretty bad shape; but I'll take you on down there."

Walker Lambright was a thirty-four year old husky sawmill worker who had never been in trouble with the law. His wife Angie was twenty-nine. They had five children.

"Mr. Lambright, if you need to wait until the doctor gets here—"

"No, Sheriff! I need to go with you."

Karl jumped into the car and pointed the way. The house was two miles up the narrow dirt road which was partially covered with low hanging tree limbs. Several of Walker's neighbors had gathered in the front yard of Walker's house, and a few were peeking at the body through the kitchen window. Jess parked in the front yard and the two men entered together. Karl seemed reluctant at first, but after taking several deep breaths he followed Jess to the kitchen.

Walker's body lay on its side on the floor. The floorboards apparently sagged slightly under the weight, causing blood to pool at that spot. A small stream of blood ran from the body toward the cook-stove.

"Mr. Lambright, did Angie say how it happened?"

"She said he just took the shotgun off that deer-horn rack above the door to the bedroom there. Then he stuck it to his chest and pulled the trigger."

Jess noticed that someone had returned the shotgun to the gun rack above the kitchen door.

"Well, that don't sound reasonable, Mr. Lambright. Why would Walker shoot himself?"

It was very difficult for Karl to look at his son, so he turned away from the body as he spoke. "I don't know Sheriff," said the old man sadly. "It don't make no sense at all. He had a good wife and family. He was a good boy. A hard-working boy too! He only had one fault that I know of."

"What was that, Mr. Lambright?"

"Well, Angie is a real nice looking woman, and Walker was very jealous of her."

"Did he have a reason to be jealous?"

"No, not that I know of."

"I'd like to talk to Angie."

"I had rather you not talk to her just yet Sheriff. She's had a bad shock over this."

"Well, I can understand that."

Jess was about to ask another question when his thoughts were interrupted by Homer Williams' speeding car followed by an ambulance. Both cars drove into the yard. Five men rushed into the house: Chief Deputy Homer Williams, Justice of the Peace B. C. Hall, and County Health Officer Dr. R. E. Henderson, and two ambulance drivers.

Homer Williams was the first to speak. "What in the world happened here?"

Jess pointed to Walker's body, which was lying in a semifetal position on the floor.

"Homer, Walker Lambright is dead. He has supposedly shot himself. His wife and kids are up at Mr. Lambright's house at this time. Angie told Mr. Lambright that Walker shot himself. She saw him do it."

Dr. Henderson slowly walked around the body jotting information in his note pad, then kneeled down beside the body and carefully examined the wound to Walker's chest. Walker Lambright was laying on his left side, his knees slightly drawn up. A stream of blood, aided by a slope in the kitchen floor, had pushed it's way toward the stove. The blood stream had come to an abrupt end about eight feet from the body. There it had begun to coagulate. Walker's right hand lay soaked in sticky blood. He was fully dressed.

Dr. Henderson removed Walker's bloody shirt and noticed that the wound was about the size of a half dollar slightly less than eight inches below the base of the neck. The area around the wound was black, which suggested powder burns, and indications were that the wound had been made by a shotgun.

The doctor turned the dead man over on his back. Jess stooped to see if any of the shot had come through. It had not. But he was able to detect a slight bulge where the shot remained just under the skin. Jess raised up and said "Doc, when we get the body to your office, I want you to push a probe through the wound. I want to know which direction the charge traveled. Up down or straight through?"

Jess motioned for Dr. Henderson to walk with him to a corner of the living room, away from Karl Lambright. They conversed in whispers, then returned to the death scene to make a careful search of the kitchen floor. They mapped the position of every utensil and a bit of furniture in the room.

A notched piece of lath was found near the table. It held Jess' attention for several moments, then caused another whispered conference. At the end Jess took charge of this and the shotgun which was found in its rightful place, hanging on a deer antler rack above the door to the back bedroom. He wrapped the weapon in a bolt of washed flour sacking, then handled it gingerly to Homer Williams so the fingerprints would not be destroyed.

Jess questioned many of Walker's neighbors while the ambulance attendants took charge of the body. The neighbors were milling about in the front yard, and each told a strange tale. Robert Walker Lambright and his pretty wife had a stormy relationship. They said it was common knowledge in the neighborhood that the Lambright family was desperately poor, always in need of extra money, and that they got along badly. It was not uncommon to see Angie walking around bruised and lacerated from Walker's violence toward her.

After the on-sight investigation, Jess told Karl Lambright that he could take charge of the body. Karl immediately instructed the ambulance attendants to take Walker's body to Athens. He looked sad and somewhat confused as to why the officers were taking so long to investigate a suicide. Doctor Henderson instructed the ambulance attendants to take the body to his office.

Homer Williams and Jess then began a methodical search of the house and premises. Homer carefully placed the shotgun and notched piece of lath in the back seat of his car, then turned his attention to the bystanders moving away from the house. Jess stepped into the bedroom and began searching through the closet and found a bright red party dress hanging neatly on a wire hanger. He laid the dress on the bed so he could give it a thorough inspection. The faint smell of perfume wafted from the scarlet frock, causing Jess to think it had been worn recently. When he turned the dress inside out he noticed grass stains on the back portion of the dress—highly unusual.

Jess walked out into the yard where he found Walker's father still talking to several of Walker's neighbors. Jess motioned for Mr. Lambright to walk with him a good distance away from the neighbors.

"Mr. Lambright, when did you last talk to your son?"

"Last night about nine o'clock. I got in my car and drove down to visit him a while. He was baby-sitting."

"Where was Angie?"

"I asked my son that, and he said, 'Dad, Angie takes care of the children all the time. It's hard work. And very tiresome. She told me that there was a dance over at the Burleson Club and you know Angie loves to dance. We both wanted to go, but couldn't. So, I told Angie that it would be all right for her to go and that I'd stay home and mind the kids."

Mr. Lambright's eyes suddenly filled with tears and his voice broke. He began to sob, and for a few minutes he was unable to speak.

Sweeten laid his big hand gently on Mr. Lambright's trembling shoulder. The effect on Mr. Lambright was visible, and he quieted down considerably. "Mr. Lambright, which way did Angie go to the dance last night? The Burleson Club is a good four miles from here."

"Down that path there. It's a short cut to the club and general store. Its about a half-mile down that path."

Jess wandered slowly down the path for about two hundred fifty yards-searching for tell-tale signs and clues. Fifteen minutes later he returned to the house and picked up Dr. Henderson and Mr. Hall. They got into the sheriff's car and drove toward Athens. Mr. Lambright elected to remain at Walker's house.

"It's plain to see that Walker killed himself." Justice Hall said. "So I think I'll mark it that way!"

"Suicide, hell! Judge," Jess interrupted. "That was murder! Withhold the verdict until I get through with the dammed investigation!"

"That's up to you Sheriff. But I'm very surprised that you think it's murder!"

189

Dr. Henderson agreed with Justice Hall. "I can't go along with you on this one, Jess. It's an open and shut case of suicide to me! You saw the powder burns around the wound, didn't you, Sheriff?"

"That's true. But suicide doesn't fit this at all!"

Dr. Henderson insisted, "Jess, I was with you all the time down there. I saw nothing that indicated murder!"

"Well, if you think it's suicide, Doc, then you didn't see everything I saw!"

As they neared the highway, Karl Lambright's house came into view. Walker's five year-old son was playing in the backyard.

Seeing the boy, Dr. Henderson turned to Sheriff Sweeten and said, "Jess, ordinarily, a boy that age makes a good witness. Let's stop and see what he has to say about it!"

"Well, you can ask the boy Doc, but it won't change my feelings about this case."

The sheriff braked the car to a stop within a few feet of the little boy who apparently had been crying before they arrived. He quickly turned his back to the officers before wiping his eyes with the sleeve of his shirt.

"Come here, son!"

The boy walked to the car with shrugged shoulders, and both hands in his pockets.

"Hello, son. How are you doing today?"

"Fine." answered the sad looking little fellow.

Dr. Henderson handed the boy a dime, which was the customary reward for giving information to grown-ups.

"What happened to your daddy this morning?"

"He got shot!"

"Do you know who shot him?"

"He did!"

"Did you see him when he did it?"

"Yes, sir. I saw him do it."

Dr. Henderson nodded slyly at the judge.

Jess ignored the baser attitude of Dr. Henderson and Justice Hall by not asking any questions of the boy. Instead, he patted the boy on the head and said, "Son, you take care of yourself."

The little boy smiled, then stood near the mailbox and watched officers drive toward Athens.

"Well, Sheriff," said Dr. Henderson, "what do you think of the shooting now? The boy is not going to lie about it. He said he saw it happen. And I believe he saw it!"

"No, the boy is not going to lie about it, Doc. I think he heard someone say that Walker shot himself, and he actually believes that he saw it. But I still say this is not a suicide. It is homicide!"

"You'll have to prove it to me."

"I intend to prove it to you."

At the Coroners Office late that afternoon, Dr. Henderson and Jess carefully eased the probe deep inside the wound and noticed clearly that the charge went neither up nor down. It traveled straight through Walker's chest in a level direction.

Jess Placed the barrel of the shotgun on the hole, then had Dr. Henderson raise Walker's hand toward the trigger. "See Doc," said Jess. "There is no way Walker could have reached the trigger. His finger comes about a foot short."

"Jess," said Dr. Henderson, "he could have used that piece of notched lath that we found on the floor." Dr. Henderson placed the notched lath in Walker's hand. "See, Jess, it fits perfectly."

The next day, on Monday afternoon, Jess returned to the home of Karl Lambright. Angie was still in bed. Mr. Lambright informed the sheriff that his daughter-in-law was still in a state of shock. Her condition was not good.

"The doctor just left," he said.

"All right, Mr. Lambright, I'll return the latter part of the week."

Funeral services were held for Walker Lambright the following day. Angie, clad in a nice black satin dress for the services returned to bed shortly thereafter. On Thursday morning, Jess returned with Dr. Henderson. He wanted to question Angie Lambright.

As they entered the yard Jess said, "I want you to go in there and examine her, doc. Then come back and tell me her condition."

Dr. Henderson went into the Lambright house while Jess waited in the car. Fifteen minutes later the doctor came out to the car.

"In my opinion," he said, "she can stand questioning. I could find nothing seriously wrong with her."

"I want to take her down to her house so she can re-enact the shooting for me!"

"Go ahead; she's able!"

Jess got out of the car and walked into the house. He went straight to Angie's bedroom. "Angie, I have not talked to you since Walker shot himself. There are some things in this case that are not clear. Please get up and dress. I want you to come with me and re-enact Walker's suicide for me."

"Sheriff, I really don't feel like going back there so soon."

"Angie, I insist that you get up and go with me!"

"Well, okay. But I really dread going back down there."

"I'll wait in the car for you."

Several minutes later Angie got in the back seat of the sheriff's car and they drove on to the Walker Lambright home. The place looked deserted. Jess opened the doors and windows to let fresh spring air force the odors from the house, then led her directly to the kitchen.

"Angie, some things are not quite clear to me. What were you doing just before your husband shot himself?"

"I came into the kitchen and walked over to the sink because I had to do the dishes." Angie turned her head, going through the motions as she walked.

She pointed to the door between the kitchen and back bedroom, "I looked over my shoulder and saw Walker enter from the bedroom. Then, as I turned my attention to the dishes again, I heard this horrible explosion. It scared me into dropping several plates. I looked around just in time to see Walker fall to the floor!"

The sheriff looked at Angie, "Are you sure, Mrs. Lambright, that it happened just that way?"

"I certainly am! Are you trying to insinuate that I killed my husband?"

"Mrs. Lambright, I'm not accusing you of anything. But since I know that you're lying, I'm getting highly suspicious."

Jess turned and asked Homer, who had just walked in, to go out and bring in the suicide gun.

He faced Angie again, "Have a seat here at the dining room table, Mrs. Lambright!"

Angie sat down and nervously smoothed out several wrinkles on the checkered table cloth, then she looked up and met the sheriff's determined gaze.

"Mrs. Lambright, I understand that you were the only eyewitness, so I'll have to bother you with a number of questions concerning his death."

She nodded calmly and Jess knew that he had gained her full attention. "I'm sorry, Sheriff. Go ahead, I'll tell you everything you need to know."

"You had trouble Sunday morning, didn't you?"

"Sunday, and a lot of times before that," she said drearily.

"I've questioned some of your neighbors, and they tell me that Walker beat you and the kids a lot. Is that a fair statement?"

"He was good to the children," she said in quick defense of her husband. "I was the one he always slapped around...but yesterday was different. He was already up when I got out of bed, and I could hear him moving around in the kitchen. He had the strangest look in his eyes. I asked him if he was sick, and he said: "Yes I'm sick! Sick of everything! I'm sick of working twelve hours a day for eighteen dollars a week. I'm sick you and the kids—and everything! With that he grabbed the gun, and pointed it a this chest then pulled the trigger. The gun made an awful roar, and it seemed like he stood there for several seconds. Then his knees bent and he fell over on the floor."

"That must have been pretty tough on you." Jess said sympathetically. "Now, let's see. How did he pull the trigger? With his thumb? Or was it the finger?" He watched her intently as he asked the question, and nodded slightly as she answered.

"I don't know, Sheriff. It was horrible! I just saw him grab at the gun. It was hanging on that rack up there, and then it roared. And after that, he was dead."

"I see," Jess replied. "Now, was it before you looked to see if he was dead, or afterward that you put the gun back on the horn?"

"Be—I guess it was afterward," she stammered. "I don't remember. Maybe I never touched it."

"Well, you surely touched it," he said softly. "Look, I'll show you how I know—"

Before she realized what was underway, Jess had touched the tips of her fingers to the inked pad and was rolling them against the surfaced paper. Then producing the photographs of the prints from the gun stock and barrel, he continued. "The way I can tell is that your prints overlap those of Walker's, as you can see by these pictures. And I can see that the prints are the same, so you must have hung the gun back."

For a moment, the widow was quiet, and then she said, "Yes, I remember now. I did that. I put the gun back. I was afraid the kids would get it."

"Now, Mrs. Lambright, show us exactly how it happened."

Angie took the weapon and cupped her left hand under the barrel. She gripped the stock expertly then set her forefinger about the trigger. She stood up and took three short steps backward toward the bedroom door and halted, slowly bringing the muzzle of the gun upward.

"Hold it a minute," Sheriff Sweeten said. "That's just how I thought it was. You stood there outside the door of the room and you shot him down as soon as he came close enough to you. You waited until he was right up to you, and then you let him have it."

"I didn't do any such thing!" she shrilled. "Walker came in through that door! He said he was tired of living. He grabbed the gun and shot himself and he fell right here where you see the bloodstain."

"Take it easy, Mrs. Lambright," Jess said patiently. You just take the gun and show us what he did with it. See, I'm hanging it back on the horn. Now you do everything he did, even to pulling the trigger. The gun is not loaded."

Angie slowly crossed the room and took the gun down by the barrel. She reversed it, then held the muzzle tight against her breast. She fumbled for the trigger, but was unable to reach it.

Homer and Dr. Henderson looked somewhat surprised at each other after Angie's unsuccessful attempt at reaching the trigger of the long-barreled shotgun.

Jess placed two chairs opposite the bloodstain, then asked Mrs. Lambright to have a seat. His eyes seemed to look deep into hers with an icy silence lasting a full minute. Then quietly, but with a firm voice, he said: "Angie, it's time to quit all this play acting. Walker never fired a shot. The way you held the gun, even if you were able to reach the trigger, the wound would be at an angle. We know that the wound in Walker's chest went straight in. The shot clipped out the center portion of his lung. It was fired several inches from his body. We know it wasn't pressed against his chest because of the powder burns around the wound. Maybe you had a reason to kill him, and if that's the case, now is the time to tell us."

Homer and Dr. Henderson sat watching and listening as the drama began to unfold. The suspense was about to shatter them both. Angie began to nervously squirm in her chair but stubbornly remained silent. The sheriff broke the maddening silence by continuing his theory.

"Mrs. Lambright, your husband did not commit suicide! I've got two reasons for making this statement. And Mrs. Lambright, they are both very good reasons."

Jess had the complete attention of Dr. Henderson and Homer Williams. They leaned foreword absorbing every word.

"When you walk on that path to the nightclub, your tracks will remain for at least twelve hours before being wiped out. Sunday morning when I got down here to investigate, your footprints were plainly visible where you walked down the path on your way to the dance. Your footprints were also visible when you came back early Sunday morning. But this time, Mrs. Lambright, you did not return alone. On the return trip, there was a man's footprints right next to yours. You stopped about a hundred and fifty yards from the house, then you and the man walked out to a clearing and made love. After you got through with your love-making, the man left in the opposite direction, and you returned to the house alone."

Homer and Dr. Henderson exchanged glances of utter astonishment. What was Jess talking about? Had he lost his mind?

"I'm assuming that you and your husband had an argument because you stayed out so late. So, when the sun came up on Sunday morning, he took a walk down the road. He did the same thing I did— examined your tracks and found the man's tracks. Then he found evidence of what you and the man had done. The earth was scuffed. The grass also betrayed you. I know because I discovered your husband's tracks coming from the house.

"On your husband's return to the house, his steps became twice as long as they were when they left the house. This led me to believe that Walker was, to say the least, highly upset over what he had learned. And the result was a terrible argument with you."

Jess arose from the chair which he had taken during the questioning. He quickly walked into the bedroom and returned with the red satin dress.

"Angie, you wore this dress to the dance that night. And when you made love to the stranger, you didn't bother to remove it. You just pulled it up then laid down in the grass. I know because I found grass stains on the inside, back portion of the dress. That, Mrs. Lambright, is not all. I have long arms. I wear a thirty-six-inch sleeve. My arms are longer than your husband's were." Jess picked up the shotgun.

"Mrs. Lambright, this gun is known as a single-barreled, twelve-gauge shotgun. They call it a 'Long Tom.' Years ago, Sears and Roebuck sold these guns. It has a forty-two inch barrel. Its a good twelve inches longer than the ordinary gun. Now, I'm going to hold this gun in the same position that Walker would have held it had he shot himself.

A icy silence filled in the room. Homer Williams stood like a marble statue. Dr. Henderson cleared his throat nervously as he shifted his weight from one leg to another.

Jess placed the muzzle of the gun against his chest, about eight inches below his neck, extending the stock of the gun in a level position outward from his body.

With the shotgun in this extremely awkward position, he turned once more to Angie Lambright: "Now, look, Angie. Even with my long arms, I can't reach the trigger. I come at least a foot short. So you can see, your husband couldn't possibly have shot himself as you say he did!"

Jess sat down and remained silent for a moment which seemed like an eternity to the deputy and the doctor. His intense look seemed to have Angie hypnotized.

"Who shot him, Mrs. Lambright? Did you or someone else shoot him?"

She sat silently for a long time but Jess' eyes never strayed from hers. Suddenly she answered. "Yes, I shot him, just like you said. He asked for it and he got it."

After admitting that she shot her husband, Angie fainted. It was at least an hour before she could explain why she pulled the trigger.

"It began four years ago," she said. "One night Walker told me there was a way for good-looking women to make some money, and if I wasn't such a little fool, I'd be out there doing the same. I was horrified at the thought, but the next time Walker brought it up we had been without food for two days. There wasn't even a slice of bread for the kids. This was too much for me. I agreed to follow his instructions and become a party girl! At first I felt terrible about meeting strange men, but Walker had me convinced there was nothing wrong with it. I loved him. I met the men at the dance hall about a mile up the path. When I returned at three o'clock in the morning, Walker was still awake. And he seemed anxious about me until he learned that I only made three dollars. This infuriated him. To avoid his abuse I went in the children's room and stayed there. Sleep was impossible that night. I was up early the next morning before he was awake, and started breakfast. When he heard me washing dishes in the kitchen, he got up from the bedroom and called me a dammed whore. I went all cold inside. Then my eyes lit on the gun. I knew it was always loaded. I grabbed the gun. It was fortunate for me that I did, for just then he appeared in the doorway with his fists clenched. Right then I knew what I had to do. He called me that bad name again, and I pushed the gun forward and pulled the trigger. When I saw he was dead, I felt as though I had just come from a refreshing bath. I felt clean all over."

Jess placed Angie in the back seat of his Buick and was about to drive away when a stranger drove past. Suddenly the man stepped on the brake, then backed his truck into the yard. He stopped within three feet of the sheriff and hollered out the window:

"Howdy, Sheriff. What in the world brings you over the county line?"

The three men turned and looked toward the road. There, within plain view and a few feet to the north, was a pine knob marker which showed the dividing line. They were on Anderson County ground, just a few yards south of their jurisdiction.

"We'd better call Sheriff Rogers, down in Palestine," Sweeten decided. "He'll have to take charge of this case."

Publication in the papers brought a waves of talk throughout the community. Wagers were freely made that any jury would acquit the attractive widow without leaving the box, so when she was indicted on a formal charge of murder, the grand jurors came in for a lot of adverse public criticism. Mrs. Lambright was brought to trial in the Criminal District Court on Friday, June 3rd, 1938.

Court house habitues, supposedly in the know, declared that a plea of guilty would result in a five-year suspended sentence. But they too were wrong. The jury retired for only forty-five minutes before returning with a verdict of guilty.

Angie Lambright was sentenced to six years at Goree Prison Farm at Huntsville. She was remanded to the custody of Sheriff Rogers in Anderson County but she rallied quickly from her shock and disappointment.

"I've never been ashamed to look my babies in the eyes," she told the reporter. "In my heart I have never been unfaithful to my husband or to them. I'm not a bad woman!"

TOM HOBBS

Friday April 5, 1942

Otis Stringer was a dairy farmer who lived on a two hundred acre farm in the northern part of Henderson County. At approximately eight-thirty in the afternoon he was in the barn milking cows when he heard his rooster crowing. At first he thought there might be a coyote in the neighborhood, but when he looked up, he noticed a light coming through the barn window.

Now that's strange, Otis thought to himself. The sun went down over an hour ago. He walked to the window and saw a huge glow about five miles to the north of his place, just inside the Van Zandt County line. He stood at the window for several minutes to see if the light grew in intensity. If it did then he'd know that somebody's house or barn was on fire.

Apparently it was. Within three minutes the glow had the whole sky lit up.

The bellowing cows would have to wait a little longer. A neighbor, more-than-likely, needed his help. So, he ran into the house and told his wife that he was going up there to see if he could lend a hand putting it out. He ran out to the corn crib and grabbed an arm load of toe sacks, then quickly soaked them with a bucket-full of water. He threw a few shovels in the back of his truck and hit the highway doing over forty-five miles an hour.

Within twenty minutes the glow had disappeared and Otis was lost. He drove around for another fifteen minutes trying to find the fire, but it was no use. He was unfamiliar with the area, so he turned around and headed home.

On the way back, and traveling down what he thought was a short-cut, Otis noticed a car parked on the shoulder of the road. It was a fairly new Buick, black in color, and two men were changing a tire. When he got a little closer, he recognized them. It was Tom Hobbs, and his crippled cousin, Jim Simms. Tom was a very wealthy landowner who lived near Martin Mills—a small town in Van Zandt County. Tom was seventy-four years old.

Otis pulled up beside the Buick and hollered out the window. "Where ye' been Tom? Over to the fire!"

The old man didn't look up. He continued tightening the last lug-nut on the wheel then asked gruffly. "What fire?"

"Well, it was over in here somewheres Tom. I've drove these back roads for thirty minutes looking for it, but I guess I took the wrong road."

"Well, I didn't see no fire."

"But, Tom, It had the whole sky lit-up! You must have seen it!"

"Look, Otis!" Tom growled, "I told you I didn't see no damn fire!"

"Well, okay Tom, but it sure had the sky lit-up."

Otis returned home and finished milking his cows; but the more he thought about it, the more it bothered him. Why would old man Hobbs deny he'd seen that fire. Perhaps he better call the Sheriff.

"Mrs. Sweeten, may I talk to Jess?"

"Just a minute, I'll get him."

Jess and Hazel had purchased a small farm near Athens at the time, and Jess was in the barn. Hazel walked to the back door then called him to the phone.

"Hello. This is Jess. What can I do for you?"

"Sheriff, this is Otis Stringer, I live up here in the north part of Henderson County. A little while ago, I was out milking some cows, when I noticed a big fire just north here. It had the whole sky lit up. At first I thought it was a house, so I put my bucket down and drove up there to see if I could help put it out. Well, on the way up there, I saw old Tom Hobbs and his crippled cousin Simms changing a tire on the side of the road. By this time the fire had gone down and I couldn't figure out which way to go. So, I asked Mr. Hobbs if he had been over to the fire. I thought he could tell me where it was. Sheriff, he just looked at me like I was crazy and said, 'What fire? 'I said, 'Why Tom, it had the whole sky lit up, you must have seen it!' He said, 'Well I didn't see no fire!'"

"Sheriff, don't you think that's a mite peculiar?"

"Peculiar yes, Mr. Stringer, but there's no law against not seeing a fire."

"I know. But, Sheriff, it had the whole sky lit up! It was just inside Van Zandt County."

"I appreciate your calling me Mr. Stringer, but Tom Hobbs didn't break the law."

"Well, it sure was peculiar."

"Well, to be on the safe side Mr. Stringer, why don't you call Sheriff Cotton Johnson up in Canton. He might want to drive out there and take a look at it."

The next morning Sheriff Cotton Johnson, drove to the scene of the fire. It was an old abandoned barn just inside the Van Zandt County line. He and three of his deputies poked around inside the charred ruins for about an hour and a half and found what appeared to be the charred intestines of a calf. Sheriff Johnson placed the guts in a gallon size jug, then took them to a local doctor for identification.

About an hour later, the doctor told Sheriff Johnson, that the guts were not those of an animal. In fact, they were human guts. Sheriff Cotton Johnson had a mystery on his hands, he had no one reported as missing in Van Zandt County. About an hour later, Cotton returned to the scene with several deputies and combed the area for evidence. Within minutes, they found a twenty-one jewel Hamilton pocket watch was—very near the spot where they had found the charred intestines. Then, about halfway between the road and barn a deputy located a pocket knife with a "B" carved on the handle. It was identified as an 'East Dallas Special.'

Johnson returned to his office and placed calls to all the adjoining counties in an effort to learn whether they had anyone reported missing.

Jess asked if he had found anything that would identify the body, and was told that he had found a watch and pocket knife with a "B" carved on the handle. Jess told Cotton Johnson that he had no one reported missing in Henderson County, but he'd let him know if such a report crossed his desk.

The story of the mysterious body appeared in the Van Zandt paper the same day the body was found. But after another article in the local paper no one claimed the remains so the jar was placed inside a two-foot square wooden casket and buried near the center of the Martin Mills Cemetery.

At ten-thirty p.m. Saturday night, April 6, Jess was awakened by two Negro girls. The youngest, Maurine Deveraux, had a baby in her arms. Both girls appeared to be in their late twenties. They knocked loudly on the sheriff's door and said, "Mr. Jess, We want to report our daddy's missing."

"Your daddy! What's your daddy's name?"

"His name is Bradley."

"Paten Bradley?" Jess asked in a suddenly serious voice. "The Paten Bradley that works for the railroad?"

"Yes, sir. He's been missing since Friday night."

Paten Bradley was a fifty-five year old section hand at the railroad. Jess knew him well. Everyone in Athens knew him. He was well respected in both the white and black communities. Suddenly, the "B" carved on the handle of the pocket knife came to mind.

"Does your daddy own a pocket knife?"

"Yes, sir. He carved his 'nitial on the handle, so nobody would steal it like the last one."

"Does he own a pocket watch?"

"Yes, sir, a twenty-one jewel Hamilton pocket watch."

Jess asked the two girls to wait in his car while he made a quick phone call. He called Sheriff Johnson and told him that he had two girls who could identify the watch and pocket knife. Johnson was to meet him at the courthouse in Canton, Texas within thirty-five minutes.

Jess headed toward Canton with both girls sitting in the back seat. They had no idea where they were going, but when he turned north on Highway nineteen, they became anxious.

"Where is our daddy supposed to be?" she asked politely.

"Your daddy's dead!" Jess said without thinking about his choice of words.

When both girls began sobbing, Jess realized he had been a little to blunt in telling of their father's fate. So he waited until they composed themselves, then speaking in a more respectful manner said, "Are you suspicious that somebody wanted to hurt your daddy?"They looked at each other for a moment, then the youngest girl said, "Should we tell him?"

"By damn, you better tell me!" Jess said angrily.

"We suspicious Tom Hobbs."

That was the second time the name Tom Hobbs had been used in a conversation. For the next eighteen miles the oldest girl, told an almost unbelievable story about Mr. Hobbs and their stepmother, Mrs. Dora Watson Bradley.

Her stepmother, Dora Watson, at the age of sixteen, went to work as a washerwoman on the Hobbs plantation in Martins Mill. Tom Hobbs was fifty-years-old at the time, and was not ready to stop "sewing his wild oats." He saw the pretty brown-skinned miss and fell in love with her. Dazzled by his wealth and by the attentions of such a prominent white man, the young colored girl fought Hobbs' advances for a while, but eventually ended up being the victim of his seduction.

For twenty years she was his mistress. Over the years young men would come to court her, but she managed to spurn their attentions. For a short period of time she lived in Tyler, Texas at Hobbs expenses; finally she moved to Martin Mills, then to Athens in one of the houses owned by Hobbs' son. She did not have to work. Hobbs furnished her with the needs of life and provided well for her.

It was in 1941 that she fell in love with Paten Bradley, who had been married three times already. When he asked her to marry him, she at first refused, feeling that it would not be right with Hobbs. Finally she gave in to the attentions of Bradley. When she told Hobbs that she was going to marry Bradley, Hobbs objected strenuously and begged her not to do it. Nevertheless, Dora told him that she felt she should have a husband and that she had remained an "old maid" for his sake long enough.

If this story was true, Jess thought, it would be greeted in Henderson County with the same enthusiasm as a squadron of Japanese dive bombers. A white man dating a black woman! He could see it now. A whole flock of reporters running back and forth between two counties, yakking like a gaggle of geese.

Cotton Johnson presented the watch, and both girls immediately identified it as belonging to their father. He pulled the knife from a separate envelope, and again both recognized it immediately. Jess instructed the girls to wait in the office across the hall while he talked to Sheriff Johnson.

"Well, Cotton, we know who the victim is. It's ol' Bradley. He worked for the railroad in Athens."

"Well, where do we go from here?" Cotton asked.

"It's your call, but if it was me, I'd send the remains down to Austin and try to find out what killed him. Then I'd go talk to Tom Hobbs."

"Tom Hobbs!"

"Yes, Tom Hobbs."

"Jess, I can't just go out and pick up Tom Hobbs! Hell, that man owns half of Van Zandt County!"

"I know, Cotton, but he's your man! Tom Hobbs killed Paten Bradley."

The next week, when Bradley's oldest daughter learned that no action had been taken in Van Zandt County, she quickly notified her dad's sister Pearl Barker. Pearl, notified a neighbor, Tillie Howard, who in turn notified her employer, Hugh Duncan Henderson, a white florist.

Hugh Henderson suggested that they all go to Sheriff Sweeten and ask him go see what Sheriff Johnson was doing about the death of Paten Bradley. Bradley's remains still lay buried in the white cemetery and no action had been taken by the Van Zandt County sheriff to solve the case.

Jess agreed to help, then drove to Martin Mills. He was followed by a number of friends and relatives of Paten Bradley who wanted to make sure that no hanky-panky was going on. The party that followed the Sheriff included: J. L. Newbill, Constable Pete Woods, Mrs. Rosa Bailey and Leroy Watson, a cousin of Mrs. Dora Bradley.

At 3 p.m. that Sunday afternoon, the caravan arrived in Martin Mills. Jess spoke with the owner of the funeral home and ordered the remains dug up. Martin Mills was out of Jess' jurisdiction but when Jess Sweeten wanted something dug up, it got dug up.

After the remains were dug up, Jess took the jar to Athens, then sent a deputy to pick up Bradley's wife for questioning.

He questioned the woman for the remainder of the afternoon, but she denied knowing a Mr. Tom Hobbs. She also denied that she had ever worked for the man.

"Mrs. Bradley, I know the whole story," Jess said looking the woman directly in the eyes. "And you know you wouldn't be in my office if I didn't know. So let's not waste any more time."

"Mr. Jess, I can't sit here and tell you that I know somebody when I know for a fact that I don't know him. I've never even heard of that white man."

The questioning of Dora Bradley was going nowhere. So Jess drove her to Canton, Texas where the questioning continued.

"Where were you on Friday April the fourth?"

"I had went to Canton."

"You knew your husband was missing, and yet you went to Canton?"

"I didn't think nothing was wrong. He was coming up here himself on Saturday night."

"Did you stop in Martin Mills and pay a visit to Tom Hobbs?"

"I doesn't know Mr. Hobbs. I done already said that."

Jess questioned Dora Bradley for another three hours without success. It was time to pick up the old landowner. Jess stepped into Cotton's office and said, "Cotton, I want you to send a deputy over to Martin Mills and pick up Tom Hobbs."

"Jess, if you're wrong about this—"

"I know, Cotton. But he's it! Now, you send a deputy over there and get the man. I'll question him. That way, you're off the hook if we're wrong about Mr. Hobbs."

Cotton quickly ordered his deputy to pick Hobbs up for questioning.

"I have a plan," Jess said, as he placed the jar of guts near the center of Johnson's desk. "Now, here's my plan. I want the deputy to lead Tom down the hall past Dora Bradley. Make sure he sees me in there talking to her. Have Tom wait in your office. Then, I'll go to your office and sit down at your desk.

"What do you want me to do?" Cotton asked.

"You just stand off to one side and watch the damn fireworks."

Within twenty minutes, the deputy led Tom Hobbs down the hallway, past Jess and Dora Bradley who were sitting across from one another at a table in the holding room. A look of bewilderment suddenly appeared on the old man's face. Minutes later, Jess walked into the office and took a seat behind Johnson's desk.

He leaned back in Cotton's chair with his eyes frozen on the old landowner. Except for a squeaky ceiling fan an icy silence filled the room, growing longer and longer as Tom's gaze ricocheted from jar to doorway, from jar to window, from anything but the glass-enclosed evidence of foul-play.

"What's this all about Cotton?" Tom asked silently.

Jess pointed to the jar of guts.

"Recognize ol' Bradley there Tom?"

Again Tom looked at the jar.

"Yeah, that's ol' Bradley! Jess said. You took him out to the barn. You killed him. Then you set the barn on fire and that's all that's left of him! Do you recognize him Mr. Hobbs?"

"I don't know what you're talking about!"

"Oh, yes, you do, Mr. Hobbs! You know exactly what I'm talking about! Dora told me everything!"

Tom's face turned a ghostly pale color. He dropped down in the chair near the door as though he was exhausted. Then, looking sadly toward Johnson, he said in a barely audible voice: "What shall I do now, Sheriff?"

Without giving Cotton a chance to speak, Jess said, "Just tell the damn truth, Mr. Hobbs! That's all you got to do!...Just tell the damn truth about it!"

Positive that Jess knew the whole story, Tom Hobbs confessed to a gruesomely choreographed murder which he and his cousin Jim Simms had committed.

On Friday, 3rd, according to his confession, Hobbs had gone into the Stirman Drug Store to buy a bottle of strychnine. He told the pharmacist that he had to poison some rats. He also bought a portion of saccharine to kill the bitter taste.

As soon as he had the poison in hand, he sent word to Paten Bradley at the Cotton Belt Railroad, saying he wanted to see him because he was "about ready to sell that property to him." His message was that he wanted to take Bradley to see the land.

Tom picked Bradley up at the depot, then drove a short distance on the road to Cayuga, Texas. Hobbs stopped the car and said that he had some soft drinks which he had purchased. They were kept in a metal box and surrounded with crushed ice. He gave the orange soda to Simms and the Royal Crown Cola to Bradley.

Having no idea that there were any evil thoughts in Hobbs mind, Bradley drank the R C Cola without hesitation. It was not long before he began to complain of stomach pains.

"Haven't you ever had that feeling before?" Tom joked.

Bradley said this was the first time in his half-century of life that he ever had such a stomach ache. He wanted to go back to Athens for a doctor. Hobbs ignored his suggestion and continued driving.

Bradley became worse and worse. He began moaning and groaning, begging Hobbs to turn back so that he could be treated. Bradley, doubled over with excruciating pain and groaning louder and louder, began to squirm and twist with the pain, but Hobbs ignored Bradley's pain and kept driving. Tom turned around just in time to see Bradley go into a series of convulsions before gasping his last breath.

Convinced that Bradley was dead, Hobbs pushed him down on the floor between the front and rear seats. Then he drove to Van Zandt County, where he found a remote and vacant barn. He dragged Bradley's body into the barn and saturated it with five gallons of kerosene, and then set the barn on fire.

"Jess," interrupted Cotton Johnson excitedly, "he killed Bradley in Henderson County!! This is your case!"

After taking the confession from Tom Hobbs, Jess questioned Dora again, using the same tactic.

"Dora, Tom Hobbs told me everything. You sat there and lied to me. Now, let's hear the truth."

She shamefully lowered her head. "Yes, I went with the white man, but I didn't love him. I went to Waco with him the other night to get me a pair of shoes, but he didn't even touch me all the way. To tell the truth, I really don't feel much bad over my part of it because I didn't do anything wrong while me and Paten were together."

She said she knew the white man years ago when she used to do the family's laundry, but that she couldn't remember how long she had been intimate with the man. But she adamantly denied any knowledge of the murder.

Mrs. Bradley had no visitors to the jail except a swarm of newspaper reporters that came from every major city in Texas. She was very upset that not one of her friends or relatives had showed up since she was placed in custody. Although she was kept in jail, no charges were filed against her. And when asked why by an Ebony magazine reporter, Jess said that she had been picked up as a suspect, but a confession from Hobbs and Simms had absolved her of any blame in her husband's murder.

"What made her a suspect?" the reporter asked.

"She knew Bradley was missing, but she didn't bother reporting it."

The jar of intestines was sent to Austin. The report proved that Paten Bradley's death was due to strychnine poisoning.

Paten Bradley had been married four times. He was a very gentle man, a Christian, and ignored the stories of the seventy-two-year-old white man's association with his wife. Dora and Paten Bradley had been married for eighteen months before his death, which was caused by a lovesick rival's trick of death by soft-drink poisoning.

Many in Athens were of the opinion that this case was almost as gruesome as any in the history of Henderson County, with the exception of the McGehee murders of 1932, a case which made Sheriff Sweeten famous throughout the world.

District Attorney Tom Pickett and County Attorney Jean Day represented the state. W. D. Justice and Homer Moore of Athens and

Senator Clay Cotton of Palestine represented the Defendant. District Judge Sam Holland presided.

Tom Pickett, vigorously prosecuted the case, but a woman doctor from Ft. Worth, Texas testified that sex had been Mr. Hobbs' problem all along. She testified that she had personally castrated Tom Hobbs, and had closely observed him for a period of three months, and now he is "perfectly normal" in every respect.

Jess asked to see proof of her testimony.

"Your honor, a doctor can lie like anybody else. Why don't we take Mr. Hobbs in the back room and pull his britches down. Let's see for ourselves whether the man has been castrated or not!"

"Sheriff," said the judge, "I have the testimony of a doctor! That won't be necessary!"

"Your honor! Sex is not Mr. Hobbs' problem! He's a cold blooded murderer! That's his problem!!"

Tom Hobbs beat the case.

Hundreds of letters poured in to Sheriff Sweeten's office asking that he run for governor. But when asked by an Ebony Magazine reporter, he just smiled and said, "I'm a lawman, I have a job.

"GERALD JOHNSON DIED MEAN!"

Mean? Hell, Gerald Johnson was one of the most vicious, most violent killers in Texas history. He was thirty-four years old in 1943, and had twice been sentenced to die in the electric chair. He had bludgeoned the life out of an old man and woman, had murdered a fellow-convict in Huntsville State Prison, had slashed a guard almost to death, and had broken out of the penitentiary. He had 430 years in sentences still to serve, and was wanted on thirty more hijacking charges in the Dallas-Ft. Worth area alone.

One of his death sentences resulted from an armed robbery in Waco, his home town. After cleaning out the cash registers on that job, he grabbed an arm-load of bakery-counter cakes, then lined eight clerks against the wall.

"You folks look hungry," Johnson Snarled. "So I want everybody to start eating. I mean You're gonna eat every damn cake in this store, and the first som-bitch that stops eating for so much as a second is gonna die!"

That was Gerald Johnson. Half-insane. Clever. Mean.

He followed definite work patterns and police knew his trademarks at a glance. He usually wore gloves and always gripped the pistol in his left hand. Will Fritz, Chief of Detectives up in Dallas, pieced together another habit pattern. After pulling his Dallas jobs, Johnson would head out-of-Dallas toward the east; always at fast speed, always on Highway 175, instead of the main highway going east, always head toward Shreveport, over the Louisiana line. Police knew a lot about Gerald Johnson, but he was always one fast step ahead.

Early in July, 1943, Johnson branded a Shreveport used-car salesman with another of his typical trademarks, the kind he liked to use in auto thievery. He kidnapped the man, took his money, held him overnight, then left him bound and gagged as he made a clean, leisurely getaway with the car. Hours later, he was described by a hysterical East Texas farm woman who told officers that Johnson had smooth-talked his way into her house. He had raped her repeatedly, then threatened her life and made off with her life savings.

From all appearances, he was heading back toward Dallas again. Police were alerted. They waited for his next move....

Hobart Lasseter was in his shirt sleeves. He didn't look very proper, maybe. Not for meeting the public. But this was midday, July 7, 1943. And no one but a dude wanders around in a suit coat, at noon in July in Texas. Mr. Lasseter was neither. He was a used-car salesman in the Oak Cliff section of Dallas. Unfortunately for him, he was standing exactly where and when Gerald Johnson was ready to strike again.

Customer Johnson approached with an unusually kind smile, a totally pleasant appearance and, in one hand, a large black guitar case. He had a revolver in one pocket, a blackjack in another, and the big guitar case was filled with sad music: an automatic pistol, a rope and a Thompson sub-machine gun.

"Good afternoon sir," Johnson said with a very friendly smile. "I'd like to see a good late-model car—the best on the lot."

Mr. Lasseter proudly led Johnson to several late-model used cars that were parked near the wide front-driveway. Hobart took a handkerchief from his pocket and wiped a pigeon dropping from the door handle before opening the door. "This forty-two Plymouth is about as sweet as an old maid's kiss. It's got less than four-thousand miles on the speedometer. The motor is tight, and she don't burn oil."

Johnson slowly walked around the Plymouth kicking each tire. He kept up a chain of disarming small talk about the heat, about the St. Louis Cardinals, about automobiles and the allied mop-up's in North Africa and MacArthur's landing at Rendova.

"I like it," Johnson said with a smile. "I'd like to surprise my wife with it. Would you give me a demonstration run?"

"Why, I'd be proud to," said the salesman.

Mr. Lasseter took his customer around the block for a trial run, then stopped at a drugstore where Mr. Johnson insisted on buying the salesman a cold soda water.

"She runs like a Singer sewing machine" said Johnson." Why don't we drive it over to my house so my wife can take a look at it. If it meets with her approval, we've got a deal."

"That's a good idea," said Lasseter. The salesman quickly turned the automobile south on Jefferson Avenue as Johnson instructed. "How far is it?"

Suddenly, Gerald Johnson's smile was gone. A pistol was in his hand and pressed against Hobart Lasseters ribs.

One mile beyond the city limits, the shaken salesman was ordered to turn off on a country road near the Trinity River. Johnson forced Lasseter out of the car and followed him through a barbed wire fence to a thickly wooded area near the water.

"Empty your pockets!" Johnson ordered.

Lasseter quickly dropped a little over one hundred dollars on the ground near Johnson's feet. "That's all I've got," Lasseter pleaded.

"Now take your hat off and get ready for it," Johnson ordered. He yanked his blackjack, started to swing it, but then stopped abruptly, as if an invisible wire was holding his arm back.

"I just changed my mind," he said. "Go stand against that horse-apple tree!" Johnson raised his sub-machine gun toward Lasseter's head. "If I was to put you to sleep for a short time, you'll wake up too fast. You'd get them cops on my fanny before I can haul it out of sight. Besides I don't have enough gas stamps to go nowhere fast enough. So I got no choice in the matter. If you need to piss or pray, this is the time to do it, friend."

Without war-time rationed gasoline stamps, it was true that Johnson could get nowhere. Without ration stamps, he couldn't buy gas. If he couldn't buy, he'd have to rob. He certainly didn't want to pull a stickup just for a tank of fuel, since it would be a sure tip-off to the police of his route.

But Lasseter was a salesman even to the bitter end. Sweating and dazed, he began talking rapidly. He didn't bother with prayers just then.

"Look, mister," he said, trying to mask the fear that dried his mouth. "Look, you missed a couple of things. I know about them. I have a family. I don't want to die. I can help you. I can help you get away fast. But you've got to let me live though. Just let me live, in return."

"Huh?"

The salesmanship had taken hold.

"Sure, I'm not lying to you. Why would I lie to you now? Look, there's another $50 in my shirt pocket. The right pocket. You overlooked it before. Take it. Take it all. It'll help you get away better. Also, I've got a bundle— a whol' bundle— of ration stamps, locked up in the glove compartment of that car. Take it all. Just let me live for God's sake."

Generosity overcame the killer when he checked both the pocket and the glove compartment. He had $172 in cash and enough ration coupons to carry him to kingdom come.

He went back to the guitar case, took out a heavy rope and tied his victim to the tree. With a walloping punch of his blackjack for good measure, Gerald Johnson left the salesman drooping unconsciously.

Cut from rope burns and hoarse from yelling for help, Hobart Lasseter wrenched his way free after a furious struggle that nearly sapped his strength. With blood trickling down his wrists and ankles, he made for the nearest house and called the police.

From the description, when it was passed along to him, Inspector Fritz knew just who had stolen that green sedan. There was still a good chance of nabbing Johnson on his way to Shreveport. Chances were that Johnson had even stopped over in Dallas for a couple of hours before starting out for Louisiana. Will Fritz played his hunches fast. He had the alarm flashed all along Highway 175.

Even though the afternoon sun was getting set to call it quits for the day, Athens, Texas, was still steaming under the July heat. Dusk was about an hour away, but the sky was still heavy with a fever of over a hundred degrees.

Jess was alone in the county jail office lobby, letting the big fan slap at the sweat on his face, when the police radio began droning out the bulletin information on Gerald Johnson. The mechanical mouth repeated everything slowly. Athens, seat of Henderson County, pulls in Highway 175 from the west, winds it half-way around the courthouse square, then sends it on toward the southeast, aimed at Jacksonville in Cherokee County. It is perhaps half the distance from Dallas to Shreveport on the twisting secondary route. That meant Jess had a good chance to tangle with the killer.

All three of his deputies were out on calls, so he loaded up his car and drove to where Highways 175 and 31 forked into the western edge of Athens. He pulled off the road and waited, settling for a handkerchief now to mop the sweat.

Behind him, on the rear floor, under the drivers seat, was a .30-30 rifle, and up front were four fully-loaded pistols. Two .45 automatics, carrying clips of seven bullets each were strapped around his waist with a fully loaded ammunition belt. Two .44 snub-nosed specials, both six-shooters, lay on the front seat next to his right leg. Jess checked each weapon, then checked them again. Everything was in order. But, wait a minute, he thought. Where is my shotgun?

Quickly, Jess drove to the service station and called Hazel. "Sugar, find Homer Williams and tell him to bring my shotgun out to the Forks. I'll be out here waiting for Gerald Johnson."

Hazel hung up the phone, then quickly placed calls to several places that Homer was known to hang out when he returned from other towns. Meanwhile, Jess drove back to the Forks and parked just off the road.

Homer was Jess' chief deputy. He had been to Brownsboro earlier that day and Hazel knew that when the deputy returned, he'd usually stop at the cafe for a cup of coffee.

"Jack, this is Hazel Sweeten. Is Homer Williams there?"

"Just a minute Hazel, I see him parking the car."

Luckily, Jess had gotten to The Forks without wasting time. He'd been there less than five minutes when Johnson came barreling down the road. Johnson wasn't slowing down much for the city-limit sign and he had the lowering sun right behind him. Jess squinted just long enough to see the shape and color of his car—and knew it was him.

He cut out from the road shoulder as Johnson passed, then stepped on the siren button and let the red-blinking police lights go to work. He'd pulled up almost beside him when Johnson suddenly gunned his engine to full speed. The dammed fool wanted to out-run Jess' faster Buick, and headed toward town at eighty-five miles an hour. Jess stepped on the gas and gave chase.

Johnson was trapped if he didn't get rid of the sheriff and he knew it; so he held onto the steering wheel with his left hand, swiveled his head and right hand around quickly and opened fire. His bullets punched out the glass in his rear window. Johnson fired again and again, swerving in and out of street traffic—jerking his head back for split-second glances at the sheriff, shooting wildly every time.

Coming into the heart of Athens,—dead on at the courthouse square, there was no way Jess could return fire, even though Johnson's guns were blazing in all directions. Johnson had emptied one and picked up another. Bullets splattered and ricocheted over the street and sidewalk. He would have smashed into the traffic for sure, the way he was swinging in and out at terrifying speeds, but the siren and red lights warned drivers just in time.

As if he'd gone completely mad, Johnson pushed down on the petal, hitting ninety miles an hour. Jess could see the bright flash of Johnson's gun every time he turned to fire back. The rear window was splintered into jagged holes. Johnson's bullets were spraying like buckshot, slapping into parked cars and trees like hot hailstones.

Mrs. Alton Laney was sitting on her front porch with a neighbor when one of his bullets sliced across her hip. She was lucky enough to get a flesh wound and nothing more, not that Johnson would give a damn.

The whole thing didn't seem possible. At the courthouse square Johnson roared around the corner at better than sixty miles an hour. Pedestrians and automobiles scattered in every direction.

Down the square they raced at over eighty miles an hour. Johnson quit firing to take the next turn on two wheels. The rubber screamed and he almost overturned, but miraculously kept his lead. At the next corner he swerved off to the right, making the turn by cutting in front of a big watermelon truck. The truck stopped dead, blocking Sweeten's way. Its driver had heard the siren and just flat stopped. Jess slammed the wheel hard to the right, brushing between the truck and the curb, missing neither by more than inches—and made it while doing seventy. He would have been flipped over if he'd even glanced that curb with a tire.

Homer rushed to the telephone in the cafe after the owner yelled that he had Hazel on the phone. "Homer!" Hazel yelled into the phone, "Jess needs his shotgun. He's at the Forks east of town. He's after Gerald Johnson!"

Homer dropped the telephone on the counter. He could hear a siren in the background, but no sooner than he dropped the phone, he picked it up again. "It's too late Hazel,"Homer shouted. "They just went through town at 90 miles an hour. I've got to go. They're shooting at each other."

Homer jumped into his car but was never able to catch up. The traffic was very heavy from all the people going home after work.

Johnson was sticking to Highway 175, taking the street that would lead him to it and gambling on giving Jess the slip or killing him.

The highway was a good road. Clear for twenty-seven miles down to Frankston on the way to Jacksonville. Jess had to catch Johnson somehow before he got that far.

From both directions, traffic was thick and slow on the south side of town. Johnson's car rocketed from one side of the street to the other, barely missing one obstacle after another. To stay with him, Sweeten had to take the same chances without having time to think about them, and keep one foot on the siren while the other pressed on the gas petal. One hand on the wheel, the other out the window. They began shooting back and forth heavily. Jess wasn't hitting much but neither was Johnson. Jess was too busy manipulating his feet and hands to flinch when he saw the red flashes of Johnson's pistol aimed at him from ahead.

Careening in and out, they hit the highway doing over ninety. One of Sweeten's pistols was emptied. He threw it on the seat next to him and grabbed up the second .45. He emptied that one inside of a minute, then began firing one of his .44s.

If Johnson couldn't kill the sheriff, his only hope was to get far enough ahead so that he could slow down to turn off on a farm road. The thick red dust that lies on those side roads in July would have covered his car and would have choked Jess out if he tried to follow, giving him a chance to loose the sheriff.

So he pushed his luck to the limit, trying to build up that lead over the big sheriff. He passed a car going up hill. A big Packard came over the rim of the hill from the opposite direction, facing Johnson head on. But Johnson didn't give an inch. He would have been smashed to shreds right there, but the Packard flew off to the shoulder, almost flipping over, just barely getting out of Johnson's crazy path. Jess felt a rush of sweat crawl down his skin and knew whoever was in that Packard must have lost ten pounds that very moment.

One of those red blasts suddenly exploded through his car shattering Jess' side of the windshield. Another shot shattered the passenger side. Seconds later, two more shots ripped through the passenger side. If a deputy had been with him, he'd have killed right then and there. Splintering glass chopped and stung at Jess' face. He lost his temper and fired out the rest of the .44 cylinder. That left the sheriff with only one more pistol.

Both lanes of the highway were bristling with vehicles of every size and speed. Johnson gambled on each curve and hill. Most of the time the siren opened up hair-breath holes, many of the cars pulling off to the dirt sidings. But they were coming at other drivers so fast that the outlaw and the pursuing sheriff were charging past them almost as soon as they heard the law horn wailing its warning. On a clear road Jess could have outrun the killer by a good ten miles an hour. He knew he could do a hundred and eight miles per hour in the Buick. But traffic was too thick, he kept getting bottled up. He had to concentrate on too much at once.

All of a sudden, it was the sheriff's turn to take a wild gamble. Johnson had managed to whip around a car, leaving Jess behind on a dangerous hill. He had to close that gap, but fast.

There was a long plodding log truck burrowing down the opposite lane. Jess realized it would come up even with the car he had to pass just about the exact instant he would get there.

Risking everybody's life, he jammed his foot on the siren button and headed right up the yellow highway line at well over ninety. The truck didn't budge an inch. Not fast enough anyway. The car Jess was passing just did manage to swerve off to the right. Jess roared between the car and the big truck like a man being shot through the mouth of a cannon and then had to slam on the brakes to take a sharp curve at over seventy miles an hour. His car swung off to the left side of the road, then back on again, churning a large cloud of dust. Then Sweeten bore down on Johnson, floor-boarding the pedal.

Soon the sheriff's fourth pistol was shot out. He had to hold the wheel with his left hand, keep his eyes on the highway at full speed, pull out the shells from the back of his belt and load them one at a time into a .44. The pistol was on the seat next to him. He had to work the cylinder around until all six shots were filled up.

Every time he tried to catch up to the maniac, Johnson would slide his car around the road, or duck around the traffic, or fire back to keep Jess from getting close. Jess kept pumping shots into the back of Johnson's car. He tried to blow a hole in Johnson's tires, but Johnson was jockeying back and forth, making a clear shot impossible.

Jess fired out his re-filled cylinder, loaded again and fired out again. He felt around to the back of his belt. One bullet was left. That's all he had.

Just one bullet. Jess had to make it count. He couldn't waste it. The only way to stop Johnson was to force him off the road somehow. But how?

He couldn't shoot him off. He couldn't use a short cut. He couldn't catch up and aim slowly. There had to be a way .He wasn't about to give up the chase. As far as Jess was concerned, his life wasn't worth a boot full of gully wash unless he could stop Johnson somehow.

And then suddenly, there was his chance. Johnson and the sheriff were in the clear on a flat straight stretch, with no other cars in sight. Jess cut the siren and pushed down on the pedal until the muscles in his feet ached. Johnson began shooting again as Jess gained. But the sheriff kept coming. He slammed into Johnson's rear bumper, almost turning himself over before punching the floor brake. Johnson's car bounced and almost overturned. But then it bounced again, righted itself, and kept going at a furious speed.

There was a fresh batch of traffic. Jess had to slow up a little. He kept both hands on the wheel and waited to bash Johnson again. They had raced almost twenty-five miles. Frankston was two miles away. Time was running out. Maybe Johnson was riding with a full arsenal. Jess didn't know. He just knew he had one bullet left and he had to kill Johnson with it if necessary.

When they got into the clear again, Jess charged and slammed him again. This time Johnson swerved at the last second. Jess only got a glancing butt at the killer's left rear fender. Johnson careened off the highway. His car seemed to stagger, then he was back on the road running again.

There was a turn and a hill. Johnson gambled blindly. He shoved through the traffic on both sides at the curve, went up the hill in the left lane and disappeared over the rim before Jess could catch up.

On the other side, at the bottom of the incline, a farm road cut off to the right. Johnson saw it and figured he could beat the sheriff to it. Jess gunned to full speed once more, coming downhill behind him. Jess was just slowing for the sharp turn when his car plowed into Johnson's at an angle. The Plymouth spun and slid, rolled over once and went sliding into a dried-out pasture. Jess' car swayed from side to side, held its balance and kept going while he aimed it toward the pasture. It plunged in through a wire fence. Jess yanked at the emergency brake and jumped out before his car   even stopped.

Johnson was somewhere in the middle of a big red cloud. Dirt and dust had kicked up into a mountain of reddish thick smoke screen that covered the man and his entire car.

Jess had the .44 ready. He moved slowly toward the dirt cloud. Johnson could have been dead or just waiting in there for him. The sheriff took about three steps when two shots roared out from the cloud and whistled near his head. The sheriff was an open target.

He couldn't tell for sure, but he saw what looked like a man's form in the red haze. He didn't wait any longer; he fired his last bullet.

Johnson groaned. The sheriff had hit him.

But the shot wasn't good enough. His form became clearer. He was walking out of the haze. He was coming to fight it out. He was just walking. Taking his time. Jess ran to his car, to the back seat, to the .30-30 rifle. He turned and saw Johnson still walking, pistol in his hand. A .38. But his hand was down. His eyes looked vacant. He didn't seem to see the big sheriff. He kept walking a straight path, right toward the sheriff. Jess pulled out of his way. Johnson walked past him. Two steps. Three. Then he fell down near the highway. Dead.

Blood trickled down Jess' face as he walked to the shade of a large tree. He had the worst headache he had ever had in his life. He sat down and held his head in his hands when a woman drove over the hill. She had been to the ice house over in Frankston. She had a one hundred and fifty pound block of ice tied to her front bumper. When she saw what she thought was an accident, she slammed on the brakes and that large block of ice came loose and slid down the highway toward Johnson.

Jess looked up just in time to see that chunk of ice hit the dead man on the hip. It flipped Johnson over. The poor woman screamed like a panther and rushed to Johnson's side, begging his forgiveness. Jess assured the woman that Johnson was dead before her ice had struck him.

"What happened?" she asked. Jess told her that Johnson suffered a fatal gunshot wound to the heart. She didn't see Jess' badge. She quickly ran to her car and drove away from there as fast as she could go.

Homer arrived at the scene ten minutes after it was all over, and Jess told him not to wait on an ambulance. He told Homer to stuff Johnson's body in the trunk of Homer's car and take him over to the coroner's office. He told him to be sure and call Will Fritz up in Dallas, and inform him that Gerald Johnson had been stopped."

Jess had a terrible headache from all the excitement and concentration; that and the fact he could have been killed. He drove straight home and went to bed. Homer, on the other hand, had a better idea for Gerald Johnson.

After Jess drove away, Homer stuffed Johnson in the back seat of his car, propped him up, and started to parade him all over the county. He stopped at the filling station and let his friends see the body. He'd point to the wound in Johnson's heart, then brag as to how Jess got him with his last bullet, and how fortunate Henderson County was to have such a sheriff.

At approximately six o'clock in the afternoon, the worried coroner placed a call to Hazel. He knew Jess was sleeping, but he had been waiting on the body of Gerald Johnson. "Hazel, I don't want to disturb Jess," he said, "but I can't find Homer Williams. He was supposed to bring the body over to my office, but he has not arrived, and I'm getting worried. Do you think he might have had car trouble or something."

Hazel called Dallas Cramer and asked him to see if he could locate Homer Williams. Dallas Cramer drove around for several hours and finally found him at a night club in the western part of the county. Homer was talking to a crowd of people who had gathered around his car. Homer was showing him off.

"Homer, I've been looking for you for over two hours. The coroner is waiting for the body."

"Well, I had a few errands to run."

"Jess wanted you to call Will Fritz up in Dallas and tell him that we've got him."

Homer quickly drove the body to Dr. Henderson's office then called Will Fritz who had gone home. "Is this Will Fritz?"

"Yes it is. Who is this?"

"This here is Chief Deputy, Homer Williams. I hear that you're looking for a fella by the name of Gerald Johnson."

"You dammed right I am," Fritz shouted. "You got him?"

"I shore do!"

"I'll be right down there to get him!"

"Well, you better bring an ambulance."

"Why? Is he hurt?"

"No! He's dead."

"Dead?"

"Yep, Jess shot him clean through the heart!"

Dr. Henderson told Jess later that night, that it was the most amazing death he had ever seen. He showed the results of a test which proved that Gerald Johnson had enough whiskey in him to make ten men drunk. He showed the tiny needle mark on Johnson's arm where morphine had been injected.

The amazing part was the shot the man had made that afternoon. It tore straight through Johnson's heart but the man had so much dope and liquor in his body that he continued walking for thirty yards after he was dead.

Gerald Johnson was that way. He died the way he lived. Mean!

A CASE OF RAPE

February 4, 1945 5:30 p.m.

"Sheriff!" shouted the woman's voice on the telephone,"this is Mrs. Trullios! I live just north of Crescent Heights. My fourteen-year-old niece just crawled out of the woods and collapsed on my front porch! Somebody has beat her half to death! We need a doctor! For God's sake, please hurry!"

Within seconds, the siren on Jess' big Buick had screamed a clear path out of the business district and was doing ninety miles per hour by the time his secretary placed a call to the local doctor in Malakoff.

Arriving at the scene just minutes after the call, Jess realized that the young girl's life was hanging by a thread. Without asking a single question, he carefully placed her limp and obviously battered body in the car then sped to the hospital.

Within minutes, Dr. L. L. Cockrell, the attending physician at the Doctors' Hospital and Clinic, said that there was no doubt the girl had been assaulted, and that her head was severely bruised. He reported her condition as critical. A further examination would be made to determine the full extent of her injuries. "How the young girl managed to crawl out of the woods in this shape was nothing short of a miracle!" he said.

The young girl's mother, her father and older brother sat in the small waiting room sobbing uncontrollably as Jess ordered his deputies to the wooded area. He wanted to make sure that nobody would enter or leave the woods until it was thoroughly searched for clues.

The young girl was in no shape to speak even though Jess desperately wanted the name of her attacker. Her aunt could offer no suggestions as to what might have happened, nor what part of the woods she might have crawled out of. Her mother said that she always rode the school bus home. It would let her off at the crossroads, then she would walk the short distance home. "Sometimes," the mother said, "she would take a shortcut through the woods."

After questioning each relative, Jess called Dr. R. E. Henderson, the County Coroner, to examine the girl for evidence. He ordered scrapings of her fingernails to be sent to the State Department of Public Safety in Austin, then returned to Crescent Heights.

6:30 p.m.

"I won't be satisfied with anything less than the electric chair for the son-of-a-bitch in this case," Jess told his deputies. "We'll not sleep until we find the bastard! So let's search these woods until we find the crime scene!"

Jess and his five deputies fanned out in a carefully choreographed strip method. The woods were quickly blocked out in a rectangle, then a portion of the area was carefully covered with the deputies walking parallel to each other. At the end of the blocked-out rectangle, all would turn in unison, then proceed to walk the next quadrant, each deputy inching their way foreword carefully examining each bush and limb for a clue. Fifty yards, one hundred yards, two hundred yards—then suddenly a loud voice,

"Jess! Over here!"

Homer Williams had found bits of the girl's clothing in a clearing. He also found a short length of barbed wire, and several foot prints. Another deputy found a very good print in the soft clay near a dried-out creek bed.

A few minutes before sundown, Jess ordered a plaster cast made of the good shoe print. All evidence at the scene was photographed before it was placed in evidence bags, and Jess quickly penciled a map of it's location. A general view of the location was also photographed before the evidence was touched. After gathering the evidence, Jess ordered the deputies to the highway.

"Somebody living on that road may have seen something," he said. "So knock on every door! Ask if they saw anything unusual from about three o'clock this afternoon until four o'clock. And if you men had six legs, you couldn't get me that information fast enough!"

"Where will you be?" Homer asked.

"I'll be talking to the bus driver."

Noticing that the soil in the area of the crime scene had a reddish color, and the soil where the plaster print was made was grey, he ordered samples of both areas to be placed in a separate evidence bag.

7:20 p.m.

The school principal offered directions to the driver's residence. Since the man had no phone, Jess was forced to drive the short distance to his home.

"Did you see anything unusual on the road this afternoon? Anything at all?"

"No. Nothing out of the ordinary. Just a Nigger changing a tire on the side of the road."

"What time was this?"

"Shortly after three-thirty."

"Where did you stop the bus when you let the little girl out? In front of the car or behind the car?"

"It was about three bus lengths behind the car."

"What made you notice this particular man?"

"Well! I thought to myself. I sez' there's a damn Nigger driving an almost new car! A young Nigger! Hell, I can't afford a car like that, and I'm a white man!"

"What kind of car?"

"Hit was a pretty new Plymouth. A nice car! Hit was green."

"Did you happen to get his licence plate number?"

"No, I'm truly sorry, Sheriff. I wish I could be more help."

"Mr. Simms, you've been a big help, and I do thank you very much."

Jess now had a reasonable identification of a suspect. He met with the deputies at the jail office and shared the information. Homer Williams said that a woman living just off the road also saw the green Plymouth. But the Negro did not appear to have car trouble when she had noticed him. She recalled that he was just standing beside his car sometime between three and three thirty. She only got a glimpse of the Negro as she returned from hanging out the wash, and didn't think much about it.

"Where do we go from here?" Homer asked.

"Phone every Sheriff's department in all the surrounding counties, Anderson, Smith, Van Zandt, Kaufman, and Cherokee. Tell them to call all the car dealerships in their jurisdiction. If the dealership is closed, tell them to call them at home. We're looking for a late model green Plymouth. Somebody sold that car to a young Negro man, and it's likely they'd remember him."

Jess returned to hospital.

7:45 p.m.

The girl's condition had stabilized, but her condition remained critical, and she was unable to speak at this time. Jess ordered the doctor to notify him immediately if her condition improved. He spent a few minutes with the family, reassuring them that an all out search was being conducted by officers in all the surrounding counties. He returned to his car and said a silent prayer for the girl's recovery.

8:05 p.m.

Suddenly, the call he had been waiting on:

"Sheriff, I hear you've been looking for a Negro man that bought a green Plymouth from me."

"Yes, sir! And I want him real bad! Do you have his name?"

"Just a minute...here it is. His name is Clyde Moore. He paid cash. And, if I remember correctly, he said he saved the money while he was in the Navy."

"How old is this Clyde Moore?"

"Sez' here, that he's twenty-one years old."

"Do you have an address on him?"

"I don't have the address on him, but the town is listed as Brushy Creek. That's in Anderson County."

8:07 p.m.

Jess called the Police Chief of Frankston, Texas with an order to pick up Clyde Moore of Brushy Creek. He sent Chief Deputy Homer Williams and Chief of Police Pete Wood to transfer the prisoner from Anderson County as soon as the officers had him in custody. He then called the hospital and told the father of the girl that a suspect was located, and that he had sent word for the man's arrest.

9:00 p.m.

The suspect was arrested at the home of his brother near Brushy Creek. At exactly 9:00 o'clock, Constable Nay Perry of Frankston had Clyde Moore in custody. Deputy Sheriff Homer Williams and Chief of Police Pete Wood of Athens were returning with the prisoner just four hours after the actual attack. Clyde Moore, employed by a saw mill near Frankston, admitted that he had been recently discharged from the Navy.

Sheriff Sweeten spent the next two hours questioning the suspect about the attack. At first Clyde denied having anything to do with the crime, but after Jess informed him that the girl stood ready to identify her attacker, he made an oral confession.

A change of clothes was ordered for the prisoner after his were confiscated for evidence. The prisoner's shoes matched the plaster cast prints, and samples of the grey-colored clay remained between the heel and sole of both shoes.

11:30 p.m.

Jess immediately drove the prisoner to Dallas, Texas before word of the man's arrest spread. He had faced a lynch mob before. Clyde Moore, being a negro and having brutally assaulted a fourteen year-old white girl, would surely result in mob action.

Tuesday Morning:

According to the doctor, the young girl's condition showed signs of improvement. Jess could visit her bedside. Her condition remained critical, so it would be best to keep the questions to a minimum.

Surprisingly, the girl's memory of the incident was very clear, and she was anxious to tell what had occurred the night before. The girl said that a Negro man was working on an automobile, or pretending to, as she was passing through a wooded section along that road. She said he dragged her two hundred yards into the woods and told her that he was going to kill her. She said that she cried and begged him not to. He told her if he didn't kill her, she would tell her parents. She then begged the man to let her go; that if he would, she would tell her parents that she just bumped her head. She said the man made her wash the mud from her head, then told her that he was going to put her in the car and take her off somewhere and kill her. The girl continued pleading and promising that she would not tell. He eventually left her in the woods but not before bludgeoning her face repeatedly with his fists. He thought she would die. The girl waited until she was sure he had left before crawling the remaining one-half mile to safety.

She had no idea who the man was.

Thursday Morning:

All evidence was quickly returned from Austin Thursday morning. The plaster cast matched the shoes of Clyde Moore exactly, and the mud on his shoes matched the samples from the crime scene. The scrapings of the girl's fingernail matched the prisoner's blood type.

Strands of the girl's hair were found on the sleeve of Moore's shirt while strands of Moore's pubic hair were found on the clothing and body of the young girl. Jess had enough evidence to present to the Grand Jury.

Court officials, working with Sweeten and the other investigating officers, summoned the Grand Jury that morning to investigate the case. The Grand Jury recessed late that Thursday afternoon after returning two indictments, one of them charging Moore with rape. The trial was set for February 27, 1946.

The wounds of the young girl had healed by the following week so, Jess drove her to Dallas where five men were placed in a line-up before her. To everyone's surprise, the girl boldly stood facing the five men in the line-up, then walked directly to Clyde Moore. She sternly pointed her finger at the shame-faced Negro and said, "You're it!"

February 27, 1946

Moore was brought into the Dallas courtroom February 27. He was under heavy guard by the bailiff and the famous Texas Ranger Captain Manuel T. (Lone Wolf) Gonzaullas, commanding company B, and several local peace officers as a precaution against any violence. Jess entered the building shortly thereafter. When Jess stepped into the crowded courtroom he noticed the father of the girl and her older brother seated in the front row. He motioned for the bailiff who quickly walked to the outer door where the sheriff was waiting.

"Did you search the girl's father for weapons?"

"No, Sheriff, I didn't. You don't suppose?"

"Yes, I do suppose! Now, I want you to go back in there and tell the father and brother that Sheriff Sweeten is here. Tell them I'd like to talk to them before we get under way."

The bailiff gently tapped the father on the shoulder then motioned for him to look toward the large double entry doors where Jess was standing.

"Sheriff Sweeten would like to talk to you before we get under way."

Both the father and brother of the victim graciously walked to the door where the sheriff patiently stood waiting. Jess placed a hand on the shoulder of each man, then led them a short distance down the hallway "Give me your gun." Jess quietly ordered.

"Sheriff, I don't have a gun."

"Earl, you know me! This is Jess Sweeten you're lying to! Now give me the gun!"

"Sheriff, that damn Nigger raped my daughter!"

"I know that, Earl, and I promised I'd do everything in my power to send him to the electric chair...didn't I!"

"Yes, sir!

"Well, that gun of yours would deny me the opportunity to fulfil my promise to you, wouldn't it?"

"But, Sheriff, I want to see the son-of-a-bitch die for what he did to my daughter!"

"Earl, just give me the gun, and I promise you'll get the chance. If you was to shoot him, then I'd be forced to lock you up. Now, give me the gun!"

Earl reluctantly reached inside his coat pocket and handed Jess a fully-loaded .38 pistol. Jess placed the gun in own coat pocket as they began slowly walking toward the courtroom.

"Wait a minute," Jess said to the girl's brother, "I want your gun too!"

The father turned to his son with a surprised look on his face. Both he, and his son had the same idea, and neither one was aware of the other's plan. The son sighed, then gave a loaded .22 to the big sheriff.

Clyde Moore's attorney, Mr. Landman, had entered a plea of not guilty by reason of insanity, but the testimony of two physicians called as witnesses tended to refute that defense. The state proved through the witnesses of the defense that Moore knew what he was doing.

The victim of the attack developed into one of the best witnesses in the case. She was very calm in her testimony and pointed out Moore as her attacker. She was the last to testify.

Among the witnesses called by the state were nurse Mrs. Henry Marenger, Dr. L. L. Cockrell, Dr. R. E. Henderson, Sheriff Jess Sweeten, Deputy Sheriff Homer Williams, Travis Brown, Mrs. Jake Tullos, aunt of the girl, and the girl's father.

For the defense, Mr. Landman called Ada Moore, mother of the defendant; David and Claude Moore, brothers of the defendant who were with him when he was arrested; Ada Lindsey, a cousin of the defendant, and Wakefield Moore, the father of the defendant.

The defendant showed no emotion throughout the trial and at times even appeared to be asleep.

Mrs. Marenger testified as to the injuries on the body of the girl, and also that the victim pointed out Moore as her attacker from a group of five colored men brought before her in the jail at Dallas.

Dr. Cockrell also testified as to the injuries on the body of the victim, and said that in his opinion the defendant was of sound mind. The jury needed only twenty minutes to find the defendant guilty of criminal assault. He was sentenced to death by Judge Melvin Johnson. The date of the electrocution was set for a time before sunrise on the morning of Monday, April 8, 1946, —two months after the assault .

The sentence was passed after Moore's motion for a new trial was overruled.

After the sentence was passed, the death warrant was prepared by Miss. J. D. Riley, District Clerk, and delivered to Sheriff Sweeten, who delivered Moore and the warrant for execution to the warden of the state penitentiary at Huntsville. Sweeten was accompanied to Huntsville by Texas Ranger Dick Oldham and Chief of Police Pete Wood. Unknown to anyone, Jess kept his promise to the girl's father who was one of the witnesses to Moore's electrocution. It was against the rules, but Jess felt that it was the proper thing to do.

THE DEATH OF TERRY STEEN

Friday June 15, 1945

Jess arrived to his office early one Friday morning and found a stack of fresh letters placed neatly on his desk, and all were bundled together with a large rubber band. He opened each letter with his pocket knife and read each one carefully. One in particular contained a postmark from Fairfield, Texas. Fairfield is located in Freestone County approximately fifty miles southwest of Athens. The letter was from a John Carroll.

Dear Sheriff Sweeten:
A man by the name of Terry Steen died over in your
county last December. I think his death ought to be looked into.
I am sure that you did not know the man
because he only lived in your county for a few months at
the time of his death. Steen and his wife Marie lived on
the O. E. Melton farm about five miles north of
Trinidad. After Terry died, an undertaker from Fairfield
went up there and brought the body to Fairfield for
burial the next day.
Yours truly,

J. C. Carroll
General Delivery
Fairfield, Texas

Jess tossed the letter to Homer Williams and asked him to read it. Homer read the letter carefully then handed it back to Jess.

"Jess, I've never heard that name before. Have you?"

"No, I've never heard of him either. But the letter states that he only lived there for a few months. The letter doesn't give us much to go on, so we ought to drive over there and talk to Mr. Melton in order to find out about these people.

Jess knew Mr. Melton. He was a farmer and gravel contractor. A man who was well thought of in the community. Jess and Homer drove to Mr. Melton's farm. They pulled into the yard where a pet monkey was jumping from limb to limb in an effort to protest the arrival of the strangers.

Mr. Melton walked out to the front porch and found Henderson County's two top law enforcement officers playing with his chattering monkey. He introduced himself to Homer and Jess then asked his wife to bring coffee. Mr. Melton had a large covered front porch with several oak rocking chairs.

"Sheriff, y'all pull up a chair. It's a long way from Athens and I'm sure you need to ask me some questions. Personally, I can't stand too long in one place. I got a bad knee."

"Mr. Melton," Jess asked, "did you have some people living out here by the name of Steen? Terry Steen and his wife Marie?"

"Yes, as a matter of fact, I did. They lived in my tenant house over there."

Jess leaned foreword in the rocking chair, noticing a small two room house roughly three hundred yards from the main house. It was half hidden by several large oak trees.

"How long did they live with you Mr. Melton?"

"Oh, they lived here for about six months before he died. You knew that he died, didn't you Sheriff?"

"Yes, that's what I heard. But I didn't know the man. How old of a man was he?"

"Terry was only fifty three years old Sheriff."

"His wife Marie. How old was she?"

"I'd say she was..."

Mr. Melton's wife interrupted the conversation with a tray of coffee. She sat it on the ornamental iron table and said, "Sheriff, Marie was twenty years old, but she looked to be about thirty. She wore the same old hair-do for six months. I don't think she washed it the whole time they lived here. She kept it in a bun like an old woman. Now Terry, he looked to be eighty years old. The poor thing was sick all the time. He had stomach ulcers you know. I think that's what killed him. You know, if you let an ulcer bust open, it will just spew the food all over the top of your intestines and it will paralyze them. I talked to my doctor about Terry, and he said the best way to treat an ulcer was with raw cabbage juice. I told Marie about fixing him some but she said that his doctor over in Corsicana said to fix him a glass of buttermilk and corn bread. Oh yes, and I think he said to give him a dose of milk of magnesia three or four times a day and once at bedtime."

Mr. Melton softly gripped his wife's arm. Apparently it was a personal warning to stop talking because she immediately ended her conversation with an apology for rambling. Jess continued the questioning.

"Mr. Melton, what were their duties here?"

"Farming and clearing land. Marie helped him saw up the trees. But when he was feeling bad, Will Lee, helped her with the sawing."

"Will Lee?"

"Yes."

"Who is he, Mr. Melton?"

"Will is from Corsicana."

"Did he work here too?"

"Yes, sir."

"Where did he live?"

"He lived over there in the same house they did."

"With Terry and Marie?"

"Yes, sir."

"How did Terry act when he was sick. What were the symptoms of his illness?"

"He lost weight. His color didn't look good. He was always holding his stomach, and belching quite a bit."

"When Terry died, where did Marie go?"

"She moved back to Corsicana."

"Where did Will Lee go?"

"He went to Corsicana too."

"Were you ever suspicious that their might have been foul play in Terry's death."

"No, Sheriff, I'm sure there was no foul play there. He was sick a long time, and just lingered along. No, those ulcers of his, they finally just done him in."

Jess showed Mr. Melton the letter that he received from Johnny Carroll in Fairfield. Mr. Melton read the letter carefully then handed it back to the Sheriff.

No! No! Sheriff, I'm positive that Terry died of natural causes."

"Did they have a doctor with Terry the night he died?"

231

"No. They found him dead the next morning. He had died in his sleep. That's what Marie told me."

"Do you have Marie's address in Corsicana?"

"Yes I do! I've got Will Lee's address to if you need it."

"I'd appreciate Mr. Melton."

Mr. Melton went into the house, and after a few minutes, returned with the addresses. He handed the monkey a small piece of corn on-the-cob to quieten the constant screeching then handed the addresses to the Sheriff.

"Sheriff, if you need anything else, don't hesitate to ask. I'd consider it an honor to help you any way I can."

Jess thanked the farmer then walked toward the car. Mr. Melton walked beside him until he stepped into the car.

Mr. Melton, I almost forgot, What was the name of the undertaker. The one that picked up the body?"

The farmer smiled apologetically then scratched his head. He stood silently for a long time trying to remember was unable to come up with a name.

"Sheriff, I'm sorry. I can't remember. The night Terry died, Marie came up to the house and asked me to call him. But for the life of me, I just don't remember. It was a firm over in Fairfield. It's the only one over there, so it shouldn't be to hard to track down."

Jess and Homer Williams drove back toward Athens. On the way, Homer seemed somewhat puzzled.

"Well, Jess, Where do we go from here?"

"We've got a lot of unanswered questions Homer. And the thing that bothers me the most is this: Who gave that undertaker permission to move the body out of Henderson County? What doctor signed the death certificate? What was the actual cause of death? And where does this fellow Lee fit in to the picture? We've got to find answers to those questions before we can go anywhere."

Jess though for a minute, then said, "We'll drive over to Corsicana tonight and have a little chat with Miss. Marie and Will Lee."

Marie was located late that afternoon in a very large two-story rooming house. Her apartment was the housekeepers quarters. She worked for room and board as the maid. Jess knocked on the door and a young blue-eyed blond haired girl answered the door. He noticed that her hair was not in the bun as Mrs. Melton described, but flowing loosely about her shoulders. However, she did look several years older than her actual age. And was a very plain homely looking girl.

"Are you Mrs. Steen?" Jess asked.

"Yes, I am."

"Mrs. Steen, I'm Sheriff Sweeten from Athens. This Is my deputy Homer Williams. May we talk to you for a few minutes?"

"Sure, would you like to come in? It's sorta messy right now."

As they entered the room, they noticed a man sitting on the sofa. The man politely stood and shook hands with the two officers.

"Sheriff, Mr. Williams, this is William —William Lee. He's an old friend of the family. I don't know what I'd have done without him when my husband passed away last year. He's helped me so much."

Marie removed several magazines from the sofa then asked the officers to have a seat. She excused herself for a few moments to quieten the crying baby in the other room. Homer gave Jess a strange look as she fumbled with a baby bottle that had been heating on the kitchen stove.

"I wasn't aware that you had a baby Mrs. Steen. I hope we didn't catch you at an inopportune time."

"He's six months old Sheriff. He was born about two months before Terry died. Thank the Lord, he lived long enough to see him."

"That's what I wanted to talk to you about Mrs. Steen. What was the nature of his illness?"

"Sheriff, all I know is what the doctor told me."

"What did the doctor tell you Mrs. Steen?"

"He told me that Terry was suffering from a very bad case of stomach ulcers."

"What doctor signed the death certificate?"

"I don't know Sheriff, I ran over to Mr. Melton's house and asked him to call an undertaker in Fairfield.

"Why Fairfield."

"Terry was born and raised there, and we used to live there. I thought he would want it that way. Besides, the undertaker was carrying Terry's burial insurance."

"Did Terry have any other insurance?"

"No, Sheriff. Not a single penny's worth."

Will Lee had sat quietly all during the questioning, and as Jess was asking questions of Marie, his eyes continually wandered in the man's direction. And with each glance, Lee would look away. It was as though he didn't want to get caught up in the conversation, so Jess pursued the matter.

"How do you fit into this Mr. Lee?"

"I'm just a friend of the family."

"Do you live here?"

"No. I live across town. I just came over to see how Marie was doing. Her husband was a good friend of mine."

"Are you married?"

"I'm separated. I have been for several years."

Jess turned to Marie.

"How do you make a living Mrs. Steen?"

"I clean apartments for several tenants, and Will helps with the groceries until I can get on my feet. Sheriff, have I done something wrong?"

"No, Mrs. Steen. I'm just down here investigating your husband's death. It seems that your husband's body was moved from Henderson County without contacting the Henderson County coroner's office. I need the name of the doctor who was treating your husband. Also, the name and address of the coroner in Fairfield. Do you have those addresses for me?"Terry's doctor? We have to ask them a few questions and get him to sign some papers. That sort of thing."

Marie quickly opened a small metal box then read the name and address of the doctor and coroner. Homer quickly wrote the information in his notebook.

"Now, Mrs. Steen, I may need to ask you some more questions after I talk to those men before completing the report to the County. So, if you or Mr. Lee, happen to move, I'll need to know how to contact you."

"Alright Sheriff."

"Mr. Lee, I need your wife's address also. In case I need to contact you."

Lee gave the address to Homer and he jotted it in the notebook. They shook hands with Marie Steen and Will Lee then walked back to the car. Jess winked at his deputy who seemed puzzled at Jess' line of questioning.

"Homer, are you getting as curious as I am?"

"Yeah! It's getting real curious. And I know where we're headed now. You asked for Lee's wife's address last, so I guess we'll go there first."

Jess sped to the home of Mrs. Lee. She was a rather nice looking middle-aged woman with slightly greying hair. The approach of the officers brought a concerned frown to her face, but she politely opened the door.

"Are you Mrs. Lee?"

"Yes."

"Mrs Will Lee?"

"Yes. What's wrong?"

"Mrs. Lee I'm Sheriff Sweeten from Athens. I'd like to talk to you a few minutes about your husband, if that's alright with you."

"Why, yes. Would you like to come inside. I'll fix some coffee."

"No, thank you Mrs. Lee. I'll come right to the point. How long have you and Will been separated?"

"About two years Sheriff."

"What kind of husband was he?"

"I hate to say it Sheriff, but he was no good. Always chasing after women. He wouldn't work half the time. He told me to get out and get a job, so I went looking for one. And when I found one, I came back and told him to get out. Both my daughters have a job too. We do better without him."

"A ladies man?"

"He thought so! If it wore a dress, he'd chase after it. Are you looking for him? What has he done?"

"Well, Mrs Lee, I'm not sure yet. But I want to thank you for your time."

Jess and Homer turned then walked to the car leaving the confused Mrs. Lee standing on the porch wondering what in the world the visit was all about. The two officers got in the car and drove back to Athens.

The next morning Jess adjusted his schedule for the days work ahead. Homer was running a little late because he was called to testify in Judge Dent's court. He rushed into Sweetens office, filed a few papers then asked, "What's on the agenda today Chief?

"Homer, let's go see Steen's doctor over in Corsicana."

"I've got his address right here."

Thirty minutes later, they were sitting in the doctor's office. He was a bone-thin, nervous sort of a man, with very thick glasses and large protruding ears. His looks betrayed his intellect.

235

"Doctor Thornton, I'd like to ask you some questions about a patient of yours. His name was Terry Steen. He died last December. I'd like to know what you were treating him for."

"He had stomach ulcers and acute anemia Sheriff."

"How many times did he visit your office?"

"Offhand, I would say about six or seven times. But he quit coming so I figured he was getting along all right. Then his wife told me that he had passed away four months ago."

"Thanks Dr. Thornton."

The next stop was the undertaker's office in Fairfield. The woman at the front desk told the officers that he was in his office, and that they could go right in. Jess opened the door to his office and noticed a well dressed man smoking a pipe and talking on the telephone. He had his back to his visitors and did not notice them walk in. When he hung up the phone and turned around, he was taken slightly aback.

"Gentlemen, come in. Have a seat!"

He shouted to his secretary.

"Mildred, bring us some coffee."

The undertaker scooted two chairs close to his desk then asked them to take a seat. Jess and Homer politely took a seat. Jess came straight to the point.

"Mr. Bass, do you remember going to Henderson County and picking up Terry' Steen's body four months ago"

"Oh, yes! I remember it well Sheriff."

Mildred handed the coffee to Homer and Jess then returned with another cup for the undertaker. Jess thanked her, then returned his attention to coroner.

"Did you obtain permission to move the body from Henderson County to Freestone County?"

"No, it was late at night. I didn't want to disturb any of the officials that time of night. Besides the family wanted him buried the next day."

"What doctor signed the death certificate citing the cause of death Mr. Bass?"

Mr. Bass was no longer smiling. And for the first time he realized this was a serious matter with the big Sheriff of Henderson County. His face reddened slightly.

"I guess there wasn't one Sheriff."

"Well, Mr. Bass, don't you think you're a little out of line here?"

"Well, maybe. But what's this all about?"

"Mr. Bass, I'll come straight to the point. I have reason to believe that there was foul play in Terry' death."

The undertaker's face reddened more. And he looked genuinely worried.

"Mr. Bass. Under these circumstances, I'm going to ask permission to have the body exhumed and an autopsy performed."

"Sheriff, that would be quite an expense to Henderson County wouldn't it?"

"Yes, about three hundred dollars."

The embarrassed Mr. Bass leaned back in his chair tapping his upper lip with his forefinger as if thinking of an idea that would make amends with the Sheriff.

"Sheriff, tell you what I'll do. Since I failed to clear the proper channels with the Henderson County officials, I'll foot the entire bill for the disinterment. Would that satisfy you?"

"I'll accept your offer Mr. Bass. And proceed through the regular channels in Freestone County."

The following day, Jess presented the evidence to the justice of the peace, and he readily signed the papers for the disinterment of Steen's body. Jess picked up Dr. Henderson and they proceeded toward the cemetery. The undertaker was contacted again. He informed the Fairfield peace officers that the diggers were at the grave site awaiting their instructions. Jess gave the order for the digging to begin.

It took two hours for the sweaty grave diggers to hoist the coffin atop two saw horses. The casket was opened and Dr. Henderson began taking samples. He placed portions of the stomach, spleen, kidneys, bladder, large and small intestines, plus a sample from the liver into several glass jars. The coffin was sealed then returned to the ground. Homer Willams immediately drove the viscera to the crime laboratory in Austin, Texas.

Five days later, Jess received the analysis. It stated that Steen's body contained enough lead sulfate to kill ten men. Homer was sent to Corsicana with orders to pick up Marie Steen and Will Lee. They were wanted for questioning in the death of Terry Steen.

Jess first questioned Will Lee who said that he was shocked someone would think he had anything to do with Terry's death. And said that he had no idea as to who might have been the culprit.

237

Marie Steen was questioned, and she denied any knowledge of the poisoning of her husband. So, Jess placed the two suspects in separate cells on the second floor for the night. This short questioning session by the Sheriff was to get a feel for who would be the easiest to break. After thinking about it overnight, he chose Marie as the first subject.

After twelve hours of questioning, Marie finally admitted that she and Will Lee had been intimate while Terry was still alive. She said that the two men shared her between them. And that they also offered her services to other men as a means of making additional income.

Lee was then questioned for another twelve hours on the following day, and implicated Marie in the death of her husband. He said that Marie gave her husband several doses of poison in his Post Toasties.

At this point Jess asked Homer to escort Marie Steen into the room. He had her sat directly across the table from Will Lee. Dr. Henderson and Homer Williams sat quietly at the end of the small room as they had done many times before.

"Mrs. Steen," Jess said softly, "Will Lee tells me that you poisoned your husband. Now, Mrs. Steen! What do you have to say to Will Lee?"

"Will Lee, you're lying. You're just trying to get out of it and get me into it."

The couple, had previously admitted that they had discussed future plans of marriage in a triangular affair in which the woman loved both men. One of them her husband. Will Lee turned toward the Sheriff with a pitiful look and said:

"Sheriff, Terry suffered a hard death. About a half hour after we went to bed, Terry woke me up grunting. I said, " Terry, are you hurting!" He said, "Bill—he called me Bill—I am! He said he was not sore in the chest but in his stomach. I got up and rubbed him and went back to sleep.

"Terry woke me up again and was sitting in bed and I rubbed him, and dosed off again. Later in the night, I heard him wake up again and I called: "Terry, how are you feeling?" He said he felt like he was smothering, and asked me not to rub him again because it wasn't doing any good. Terry woke up again and said, "Ahhh," and Marie jumped up. I grabbed a towel. Terry was complaining of hurting in the lower part of his stomach.

"Marie told me that she was going to get rid of Terry and I asked her how was she going to do it. I thought she meant that she was going to run him off. But she said that she was going to poison him. So I said to her. I said, you're going to get in a mess, and she said she didn't care."

"Lee, where did the poison come from?" Jess asked.

"It was at the house when her and Terry moved there."

"Who suggested the poison?"

"She did! She knew that was poison."

Will turned to Marie:

"Marie, you remember that you told me you were going to get rid of Terry?"

"No, it was not me. You did it!"

"Woman! I told you that was poison. It had been strewn on the floor from the box!"

"No, you didn't!"

"Marie! You had the poison, and I asked: Marie, what did you do?...And you said you gave Terry three doses!"

"No, you are the one who did it!"

"Woman! I'm telling the truth. I've lied long enough. You got the poison!"

"That isn't true Sheriff! He's just trying to get me into it!"

"You told me about three weeks before that you were going to get rid of Terry, and I said: The hell you are!"

"Will, you're lying!"

"I know what you did!"

"That isn't true!"

"You told me you gave him three doses, it was strewed about the floor. You went to the smoke house and got the poison, and there were your tracks!"

"You're lying!"

"Marie! The first thing you said when you woke me up was that he was dying!"

"No! You woke me up and told me he was dead!"

"You know you were strewing the stuff around for three weeks. You went down there to the smoke house and got a snuff box full and gave him three doses, I've shielded you all along and these men know I'm telling the truth!"

"You are not telling the truth Lee. You are trying to get me in deeper and deeper! I'm not telling an untruth, because I never was in it. Sheriff. He poisoned my husband! He's trying to put me in every bit of it! And he's trying to get out of it. Will! You went out and got the poison and put it in the milk with those Post Toasties!"

"I did not!"

"You poisoned him and you're trying to get out of every bit of it," repeated Mrs. Steen. "Sheriff! He gave Terry three doses, a teaspoonful each time!"

"I've told these men the truth!" Lee hollered.

"Sheriff! Will went out and got some and put it in his milk with those Post Toasties! It was condensed milk!"

"It was cow's milk," Lee yelled.

"Will! You went to the store and got condensed milk and mixed it with water. He ate two glasses of post Toasties and there was poison in it," Mrs. Steen charged.

Jess interrupted the shouting match.

"Who got the condensed milk?"

"Lee did," said Mrs. Steen.

"No I did not! I went to the store and got some snuff, but not milk."

"You went to the store and got some cheese, condensed milk— two cans—some bologna and light bread," said Mrs. Steen.

"I got some snuff, but not condensed milk," Lee repeated. "The box of Post Toasties had only a little bit in it."

"That's not true. I opened the box," said Mrs. Steen." That poison was in the Post Toasties and milk. Will put it there and told me it was sugar. He gave him a dose everyday."

"She gave him three doses in one day," Lee charged.

"He put the poison in the milk and told me it was sugar. He put it in with a spoon, Terry opened the milk and Will fixed it up," said Mrs. Steen. Terry had froth all over his mouth and I wiped it off. Will Lee first mentioned poisoning him, and I will be honest, he did it. He told me he was going to poison him about a week before he gave him the poison. And the night Terry died, the first I knew was when Lee told me Terry was dead. I jumped up and put on a dress. Nothing happened after supper. Terry was not complaining. I didn't know before that he was poisoned, but Lee told me so after Terry died. He told me so that night.

Addressing Lee, she said:

"You told me it was sugar. You put some in those Post Toasties and milk that night."

"We didn't have any condensed milk," Lee said. "We made that story up last January. We said that if we were questioned, we would tell the same story about what happened, and those are the lies I had been telling before tonight."

"Sheriff, He told me to tell you all that he did not poison Terry— that he fell out the screen door on some cans and jars," Mrs. Steen charged.

"You told me about the screen door woman!" said Lee.

"It was you that told me that!" countered Mrs. Steen.

"I told her to get the poison off the floor, that the baby might get some of it in his mouth," Lee said.

"You got the package from over the window and took it outside yourself and told me that it was poison," Mrs. Steen said. "Terry did not fall against the screen door. That was your idea."

"It was your idea," Lee charged.

"I knew he was going to poison him," said Mrs. Steen.

Jess interrupted:

"Marie, I thought you said you didn't know that Will was going to poison Terry?"

"I didn't know what to do when I found out it was poison. I didn't know anything about him dying. I knew it was poison at the time. He told me it was sugar and then later that it was poison."

Addressing Lee, she said:

"I did not tell you that I was going to get rid of him."

Again addressing Jess, Mrs. Steen stated: "I liked my husband. I did not poison my husband."

Dr. Henderson interrupted:

"A man would suffer a violent death from poison such as Steen received, and would have made considerable noise in his death struggle. A teaspoonful of the poison Steen is believed to have received is many times the fatal dose, and would bring about death in three hours."

Jess had heard enough.

Mrs. Marie Steen, and Will Lee, were both charged with murdering Terry Steen on December 9, 1944. Will Lee was found guilty of murdering Terry Steen. He received a 99 year sentence. Marie was also found guilty. But seeing her nurse the baby throughout the trial, she gained a great deal of sympathy. She was given a five year suspended sentence.

HATE KILLED RICHARD SIGLER

At gathering evidence for the defense of his client, attorney Richard Sigler had no equal, and when he and Will Justice were partners in the law firm of Justice & Sigler, they were tough to beat in the courtroom. Will Justice was known to loose as much as fifty pounds defending a client. Will was direct and straight to the point. Richard, on the other hand, let his emotions get the better of him.

At times Richard drank too much, especially after loosing to Sheriff Jess Sweeten, and loosing the last two high-profile cases had taken their tole on the young attorney.

The famous Patton case had caused a split in the partnership, plus an unsubstantiated rumor of embezzlement from the firm almost ruined Richard's reputation.

Before Jess was elected Sheriff, Richard owned a number of slot-machines, which he had placed in various businesses throughout the county. The machines turned a good profit, enabling him to purchase a substantial amount of real estate.

Slot machines, according to the state government, were illegal, so Jess ordered them removed. Richard refused, arguing that the machines were played strictly for their entertainment value only, nothing more. Jess warned him a second time. Again, Richard refused. The sheriff at that point had no choice but to confiscate the property.

Richard fought through the courts in an effort to retrieve his machines, but the state ruled against him. There ended the lesson—but the hatred of Jess Sweeten by Richard Sigler was never resolved.

Richard lived in an apartment building he owned with his mother, and a retarded brother named Harold. The apartment was located on the first floor of the building. To this day, it stands as a reminder of Richard's hatred for Jess Sweeten.

At nine o'clock one Saturday night, less than three months after the sentencing of Guydel Beckham for the Lake Trinidad murders of her husband, Jess and Homer Williams rounded the north side of the courthouse. They noticed a very strange scene taking shape under the large oak tree. Attorney Sigler was chasing a stranger with a pocketknife in his hand.

"Homer, do you see what I see?"

"Yeah," Homer answered with a laugh, "I guess the fellow didn't pay his attorney's fee!"

Jess noticed Richard's mother patiently waiting in the family car. The old woman just sat there with a blank expression on her face. It was as though she was waiting for her son to complete his work.

"That would be about right!" replied Jess. He stepped out of the car and quickly ran up to Sigler. He noticed that both men were nearly out of breath, and the stranger scared out of his wits.

"Richard! What in the hell are you doing!"

Richard stopped the chase of his quarry, then took a few deep breaths while pointing his knife toward the scared stranger. In a slurred shrill, he shouted, "Arrest that son of a bitch!"

"What for?"

"That bastard's drunk! He ran into my car and bent my fender!"

"He's on foot, Richard!"

"It was out there on the damn highway! He scraped it when he went around me!"

Jess turned to the stranger who was peeking around the tree:

"Is that true, fellow?"

No, sir! I don't drink! I was on my way to a job over in Corsicana. I passed him on the highway! and when I got halfway around him, he pulled into me!

"We both stopped out there on the highway to see about the damage, but he took to cussin' at me! I got scared, so I jumped back in my car and got the hell out of there. Then, when I got into town, he forced me off the road. So I jumped out of my car and ran. Then he pulls a pocket knife on me!"

"Fellow, I want you to walk over here and blow your breath in my face."

The stranger stepped close to the Sheriff's face then blew his breath lightly. Jess could not smell the slightest hint of alcohol.

"Richard, it's your turn! Step over here and blow your breath in my face!"

"I'm not drunk!"

"Blow your breath in my face now or by damn, you'll do it in jail! It's up to you, Richard!"

Richard staggered close to the sheriff's face, took a deep breath, then blew as if he was the top-spitter in a seed blowing contest.

"Dammit, Richard! You're drunk! Now get back in your car and let your mother drive you home!"

"Jess! I want that bastard arrested! The son-of-a-bitch bent my fender!"

Jess stepped to Richard's car where Mrs. Sigler was patiently waiting for her son.

"Mrs. Sigler, I want you to step out here and tell Richard to get in the car. I don't want to lock him up, but if he persists in making a damn fool out of himself, he's going to jail!"

Mrs. Sigler's mouth grew tight, causing deep wrinkles in her lips. Clearly upset at the way her son was being spoken to, the old woman puffed up like a blow fish and refused to budge.

Jess patiently waited a few moments for her response then said: "Mrs. Sigler! Do you want me to put him in jail?"

Her face reddened to match her hair. The mouth wrinkles grew deeper as she pursed her lips and crossed her arms. She refused to answer. Meanwhile, Richard continued his non-stop cursing, aimed primarily toward the stranger.

Jess ordered the stranger to return to his car; he was free to go. When Richard ran toward the quickly departing stranger for the second time, Jess grabbed him by the seat of the pants with one hand and the collar of the shirt with the other.

"Okay, Richard!" Jess said loudly, "Have it your way!"

Jess goose-walked Richard to the big cruiser and stuffed him in the back seat. He returned to the Sigler automobile and stuck his head through the open window on the driver's side.

"Mrs. Sigler, you can pick him up in the morning."

Mrs. Sigler again refused to look at the sheriff, or to ever acknowledge that he was at the window. She remained stoically seated, her eyes looking straight ahead.

Richard was not charged. Jess placed him in an unlocked cell on the second floor, where he promptly fell asleep. Within thirty minutes, Mrs. Sigler stormed into Jess' office with a young, slick-haired lawyer in tow, demanding Richard's release.

Jess calmly explained that Richard was fast asleep and in no danger. He had not been charged with a crime. His decision that Richard would remain until six o'clock in the morning was final.

By six o'clock following morning, Mrs. Sigler's haughty attitude had humbled somewhat. She and her younger son, Harold, sat patiently in Jess' office. When Jess walked through the door she asked politely if she would be allowed to take Richard home. Harold remained seated while Jess stepped to the door and pointed her toward the second floor. Harold waited until his mother walked out before starting a conversation with Jess.

"Sheriff," said Harold, "I was kidnapped ten days ago!"

"You were?"

"Yeah, they took me down there in the woods and shot me in the leg with a hypodermic needle!"

"A hypodermic needle, huh?"

"Yeah, and it hurt too! You need to go down there and kill 'em!"

"Well, I see you got loose from them!"

"Yeah, I cut one of them!"

"You cut one?"

"Yeah, I cut his head off!"

"What did you do with it?"

"I put it out in the street and let the cars run over it!"

Suddenly, Harold jerked backward in his chair as though he had seen a ghost. His eyes rubbered toward the coat rack where Jess kept his hat. He was giggling at something. Jess looked around to see what had caught his eye, but the only thing he could see was the white Stetson hat.

"That's the funniest thing!" Harold laughed, "I've never seen one of them before! He's a cute little feller!"

"What the hell are you looking at, Harold?"

"That little blue man! Right there! See! He's on your hat!"

"You see a little blue man?"

"Yeah! He's got a bell on his head!"

Harold Sigler's brain had begun to wander out in the deep end of the lake; the look in his eyes changed from laughter to sudden, adrenaline-pumping fear. Apparently, the little blue man had scared the living hell out of him. He started babbling incoherently, then, quick as a flash, ran out the door toward the family car. Jess wheeled his chair around just in time to see Harold dive head first through the open window, slapping his hair as though bedaubed by a swarm of yellow-jackets.

Homer had caught the tail-end of the conversation as he stepped into the Sheriff's office, and was just flat-out, chin-scratching bewildered over the whole thing.

"Jess, what in the hell was all that about?"

Jess shook his head with pity. "Homer, Harold Sigler just saw a little blue man with a bell on his head!"

"Where?"

"On my hat!"

Homer shook his head. Walking out the door, he pointed a finger toward Richard, his mother and the slick-haired lawyer who was bringing up the rear.

"Richard, don't you think it's about time to change your brother's light bulb?"

When the Sigler crowd stepped into Jess' office, Mrs. Sigler politely took a seat. The two lawyers remained standing.

"Sheriff, do I need to sign anything?" she asked.

"No, Mrs Sigler," Jess answered seriously. "But I think its time that you considered placing Harold in an institution somewhere. I've not said anything before, because I felt that he was not dangerous. But he is now, and he's getting worse."

That was not the news Richard or his mother wanted to hear. He angrily took his mother by the arm, almost forcing her from the chair, and shouted: "Sheriff! We've taken care of Harold all his life! And by God! we don't need you to start telling us what to do! Come on, Mother!"

"Okay, Richard." Jess replied, "It's your funeral. But at least take that boy to a doctor."

Neither Richard nor his mother would listen. They hated Jess Sweeten with a purple passion, and so his words of concern toward Harold were taken as hatred toward them. Storming out the door of the jail, they stalked to the car, slammed the door, and sped away.

Three weeks later the phone rang. Jess picked up the receiver and heard a woman's shrill hysterical voice on the other end.

"Sheriff! Come to the Sigler Apartments quick! There's been a gunshot. Hurry!

"Hold on a minute! Who is calling and what is the number of the apartment?"

"Sheriff, why are you wasting time when we need you out here so bad?"

Suddenly the phone went dead. The woman had rudely hung up. Jess jumped into his car and sped to the Sigler apartments. It could be a trap. Why had the woman hung up before giving the necessary information? Why would she not tell him which apartment? Valuable time could be lost because there were many apartments in the building.

Jess quickly sped to the Sigler Apartments without a hint of what he might find. The modern, up-to-date apartment complex was a neat and well kept two story building.

The entire structure was clothed in darkness. Not a single light was visible anywhere.

Jess entered the narrow pitch-dark foyer of the building. The whole place was eerily silent. Not a soul stirring anywhere. He took a firm grip on his flashlight but felt that it would be unwise at this time to switch it on. He felt his way down the right-hand wall searching for a doorknob. He eased the door open and slowly entered a carpeted living room where a mournful voice was heard in the darkness.

The wheezing, moaning voice seemed to be coming from the kitchen area. It was moving as though it's owner was just pacing back and forth across the room. Jess eased closer. The mournful voice was so close now that he could reach out and touch it. He waited until it passed, then stepped quietly to the spot where he figured to grab the person on the return trip.

Now he recognized the voice.

"Harold Sigler!"

Jess hit him with the beam of the flashlight. Harold was holding a sixteen-gauge shotgun in both hands. Harold raised the shotgun and quickly aimed toward the beam of light which had him momentarily blinded. Jess jerked the rifle out of Harold's hands, then grabbed him around the waist. He pulled Harold out of the apartment to the foyer.

All of a sudden someone flipped the main power switch, which lit up the entire complex like Christmas. A crowd gathered around the sheriff and Harold Sigler. Jess ordered a surprised tenant to grab hold of Harold. Not wanting to become involved in the matter, the strong looking fellow backed away.

"Dammit!" Jess hollered. "Hold him so I can find out what happened!"

"Sheriff, I can't do that!"

"If you don't take hold of him, I'll put you in jail!"

The man quickly grabbed hold of Harold Sigler, almost lifting him off the floor. Confident that Harold was in safe hands, Jess stepped inside the apartment again. There on the floor of the kitchen lay Richard Sigler. He lay flat on his back with a hole in his chest. The sixteen-gauge shotgun blast had made a hole no larger than a fifty-cent piece. It had been fired at very close range. Richard Sigler was dead.

Another tenant rushed into the kitchen. "Sheriff! I seen it all! My wife and I were having a shrimp cocktail with Richard. We had just sat down at the table when Harold came in through the fire escape. He walked up to Richard and said, 'Damn you, Richard. You ain't paid rent in six months!'"

"Then he shot him?"

"Yes, sir! He just walked up real close, then blam! Shot him right in the chest!"

Harold Sigler was placed in the jail until he could be examined by a doctor, and after a few days of close observation, he was found to be mentally unbalanced and extremely dangerous.

Mrs. Sigler was devastated. In one swift action, she had lost both her children. She phoned Sheriff Sweeten, pleading that she be allowed to see her son one last time before he was sent to the asylum in San Antonio, Texas.

"Mrs. Sigler," said Jess, "You have my word. I'll not allow him to be moved until you're able to come visit with him."

The next morning, after visiting her son for about an hour, Mrs. Sigler stopped by Jess' office. Her eyes were red from sobbing, but she composed herself and said, "Sheriff, if only we had listened. With all of your experience, if only we'd listened, Richard would be alive today. We hated you so much, and all you were trying to do was help. We should have listened."

"Mrs. Sigler, I'm very, very, sorry."

Hate, once allowed in the heart of man, will close all ears to reason. It will blind all logic, suffocate all hope, and will ultimately destroy the human body through the absence of love. Hate killed Richard Sigler.

The squeaky fan shuffled a fresh batch of papers on his desk. Mrs. Sigler quietly walked to her car and drove away. The air was filled with the sweet smell of fresh cut watermelon as the farmers busily went about their business in the lot across the street. And the distant whistle of a fifty-car freight train proved that, in Henderson County, life goes on.

AP Wirephoto

OLD GUNSLINGER TURNS CRIMINAL INVESTIGATOR

Jess Sweeten, 72-year-old former sheriff, must have been what Athens, Tex., Dist. Atty. Bill Green had in mind when Green recently was elected on promise to get tough on crime. The 6-foot-4, 225-pound Sweeten shot nine men and killed three during gun battles in his law enforcement career, from 1932-1955. In January Sweeten becomes a criminal investigator for Green.

LONNIE WILLIAMS HAD A BAD LEG

On Sunday February 21, 1954, the Charlie Pinkerton Drugstore in Chandler was robbed. Charlie Pinkerton told the sheriff that he had been busy filling a prescription of morphine for a man who hobbled in with a bad leg and had forgotten to lock the safe where the narcotics were kept. He recalled that only two other customers were in the store at the time, but they hadn't made a purchase. He remembered only that the woman was heavy-set and the man was thin.

"The fellow with the prescription, do you have his name?" Sweeten asked.

Charlie searched his files and came up with the name of L. C. Williams, and then remembered the man saying that he was on his way home to Paris, Texas. "But Sheriff, Mr. Williams couldn't have been the thief," he said, "because I insisted that he wrap a bandage around his leg. I helped him wrap it up, and then he left. He was never out of my sight."

"Yes, but did you see him drive away?" Jess asked bluntly.

"No. Why?"

"Williams probably set up the deal," Sweeten explained. "He purchased morphine with a prescription from a doctor in order to locate the safe. Then distracted you just long enough for the other two to clean it out. More than likely, they all drove away together."

Jess contacted an informant in Tyler, Texas several days later. The man said it sounded a lot like Charlie Woolsey and Helen Guyton.

"They hit all the little towns from Dallas to Shreveport," he said. "and Lonnie Williams often travels with them. He's a morphine head. You'll find him up in Hot Springs, Arkansas. He'll stove-up until the money's all gone."

Jess filed charges of theft of over $50 dollars against L. C. Williams, Helen Guyton and C. H. Woolsey, and sent word for the arrest of Williams to the Hot Springs Police Department.

Within two days, Jess received word that Williams had been apprehended. Included in the deal was an automobile and trailer owned by Helen Guyton. Williams waived extradition, and Jess drove to Hot Springs the following morning.

The police chief in Hot Springs had all the necessary papers plus a handcuffed Williams waiting on the front lawn of the courthouse. Although Jess thought it unusual to have a prisoner cuffed to a tree limb, he pulled over to park his car. An officer stuffed Williams in the front seat before Jess had a chance to kill the engine. Something was fishy. Jess could hear laughter coming from inside the court house. He could see several secretaries on the second floor waving and smiling as though they knew a secret. For some reason, everybody seemed awful anxious to get rid of Mr. Williams.

As Jess drove back toward Athens an odor that would gag a maggot on a gut wagon filled his car and almost choked him to death. He quickly rolled down the window but that seemed to make it worse. He ordered Lonnie to roll his window down but that helped only a little. Jess quickly brought the big Buick to a stop to check if he'd run over a dead dog. Perhaps he'd hit one and it had flipped up and got wedged between the frame and engine.

He looked under the back seat and checked the trunk. Puzzled, he continued on down the road. The smell was still there. There was no way he could drive all the way back to Athens with a smell that awful penetrating his nose. He came to the section of town where all the large expensive homes were located and stopped again.

Jess asked the prisoner to step out of the car for a minute, thinking maybe ol' Lonnie might be the source of the odor. Then he stepped back into the car and rolled the windows up. Sure enough, the smell had disappeared. Now Jess understood why Lonnie was cuffed to a tree; and why the ladies on the second floor were smiling through the open windows. They were mighty glad to get rid of Mr. Lonnie Williams.

Jess noticed a brownish color on the inside of Lonnie's right pant leg that went from his knee to the ankle. It looked as though his pant leg was stained from some type of wound. It was wet, runny and perhaps infected.

"Lonnie, pull your britches leg up," Jess asked, "and let's take a look at that."

Lonnie carefully slid his pant leg up over his knee which, exposed a huge sore that was so bad Jess could see about a foot of exposed leg bone. It was extremely red, with a mass of runny infected puss that stunk to high heaven.

"God-a-mighty, Lonnie!" Jess gagged. "Why didn't you see a doctor about that?"

"That!" Lonnie laughed loudly. "Hell! I wouldn't take a million dollars for that. That'll get me more morphine than anything. When I need me a fix, all I got to do is show this ol' leg to a doctor and he'll give me enough to last a week! No, sir! I wouldn't take a million dollars for it!"

Jess continued driving past a row of large stately homes near the outskirts of town. He could see Lonnie began to rock back and forth while holding his stomach,

"Oh! Sheriff, I'm getting sick."

Jess pulled to a stop in front of the last big stately Victorian home with a water faucet in the front yard.

Lonnie's face showed a great deal of pain. "How long have you been on morphine?" Jess asked.

"Forty years."

"Forty years?"

"Yes, sir. Forty years."

"Well, Lonnie, before I came up here to pick you up I went to a doctor over in Athens. I had him fill out a prescription for you. Look in the glove compartment there, and you'll find everything you need." "You help me and I'll help you."

To his surprise, Lonnie found a syringe, a large tablespoon and a ten-count bottle of morphine tablets. Lonnie ran to the water faucet, crushed a tablet in the spoon which held just the right amount of water, then injected the mixture into his arm. He leaned against an oak tree for a minute or two waiting for it to take effect, then walked back to the car.

"Sheriff," Lonnie said. "I'll be glad to help you in anyway I can."

By the time they arrived back in Athens, Lonnie Williams had helped Jess clear over 100 robberies from Dallas to Bossier City, Louisiana. Charlie Woolsey, Lonnie's buddy, had been an informant for Sheriff Bill Decker up in Dallas. Decker chastised Charlie for pulling a robbery in Henderson County.

"But I didn't pull a robbery in Henderson County! "Charlie protested.

"It was in Chandler, Texas...that's in Smith County!"

"Not so Lonnie!" Decker said. "Chandler is located in Henderson County!"

"Well, I didn't know that. Would you call Jess and tell him that I'm sorry about that!"

Jess Sweeten honored at retirement party

The Record

Shortly after retiring from the strenuous duties in the Sheriff's office and taking a much needed rest, Jess Sweeten accepted a position as special agent for the Magnolia Pipeline Company, a subsidiary of the Mobil Oil Company. He had been on the new job only a few days when he was put to the test.

On one of his company assignments, he ran into a rowdy six-foot-five-inch, two hundred pound giant who said, "You're going to keep questioning me until I come unwound!"

"Go right ahead, mister!" said Jess "I've had twenty-five years experience winding fellows like you back up when they come unwound!"

"Fella, do you know who you're talking to?" a friend of Sweeten asked.

"I don't know and I don't care!" said the big man.

"This is Jess Sweeten, you dummy!"

"Jess Sweeten?"

"Yes!" "The Jess Sweeten? You mean to tell me that I've been answering questions from Sheriff Jess Sweeten himself?"

The assignment was accomplished without further interruption.

There was another side to this giant ex-lawman. One that was tender and giving: "I must ask God to forgive me of my sins," he said at our last visit, "because I've sinned quite a lot in my time. Not that I've stole or anything like that, but at times...Well, I've been pretty tough."

There was a long silence, then a tear of pain rolled down his weathered cheek. Jess was seventy-five-years-old and dying of cancer, but he never complained.

Jessie James Sweeten was a good Sheriff, and a good man. He was my friend.

On September 4, 1954, Jess Sweeten was presented citation of honor.

WHEREAS, Jess Sweeten is retiring after serving with honor and distinction, as Sheriff of Henderson County, Texas;

WHEREAS, Jess Sweeten has gained nationwide fame and has become a legendary figure as a peace officer because of his fearlessness in the performance of his duty and because of his solution of some of the most bizarre and baffling crimes of our times, gaining not only great personal recognition for himself but for Henderson County as well; and

WHEREAS, Jess Sweeten has gained for himself and Henderson County, Texas, further national fame because of his feats of marksmanship with a pistol; and

WHEREAS, it is the desire of the grand jury of Henderson County, as representatives of the people of Henderson County, Texas, to recognize the accomplishments of Jess Sweeten and to express their sincere gratitude for his twenty years of outstanding service;

NOW, THEREFORE, BE IT RESOLVED by the Grand Jury of Henderson County, Texas, for the September term, 1954, that in it's appreciation and gratitude and the appreciation and gratitude of the people of Henderson County to Jess Sweeten for his twenty years of outstanding service; that the Foreman of the Grand Jury read and present this citation in an appropriate ceremony before the beginning of a Court session; that a copy of this citation be spread upon the minutes of the Court as a lasting memento of our recognition and gratitude.

GRAND JURY, SEPTEMBER TERM, 1954
HENDERSON COUNTY, TEXAS

BY: (signed)

Roy Parnell

Jess Sweeten age 70 giving a shooting exhibition for the Lone Star Steel Company employees

Peggy Ann Sweeten and Jess Sweeten visit with Sheriff Gene Biscaluz of Los Angeles, California

258

A shooting demonstration for Autie Murphy The War Hero

Backyard potato shoot. Featuring Gus Sours

A Texas Legend takes a break with Hazel and the hounds.

LYNDON B. JOHNSON
TEXAS

United States Senate
Office of the Democratic Leader
Washington, D. C.

May 7, 1954

My dear Friend:

I was reading in the Tyler Morning Telegraph
that you are completing twenty years of having served
as sheriff of Henderson County. I know that you have
many memories of your service and that your many
friends regret your retirement. Please accept my
sincere best wishes for your future in private life.

If there is any way in which I may be of service to you, I hope you will let me know. I would consider it an honor to hear from you.

Sincerely,

Lyndon B. Johnson

Mr. Jess Sweeten
Sheriff of Henderson County
Athens, Texas

On August 1, 1995 a petition was circulated in Athens, Texas for a
street to be named in Sheriff Sweeten's honor.

ACKNOWLEDGMENTS

A special thanks to my wife, Shirley Annette. And to: Ginger Lines, Linda Carpenter, Rita Kidd, Neva Tyler, Lawrence Melton Sr., Ronnie Malone, Jess Laird, Aaron Skinner, Mary Jo Yebernetsky, Carla Lee, Kim McGuire, Deborah Morris and Joan Hallmark for their support.

And to the hundreds of people who purchased this book long before it was printed...You gave it life.